The Communication Systems of the Body

The Communication Systems of the Body

DAVID F. HORROBIN

Basic Books, Inc., *Publishers*
NEW YORK LONDON

Third Printing

Library of Congress Catalog Card Number: 64-24590
Manufactured in the United States of America
Designed by Sophie Adler

Contents

Illustrations

The Communication Systems of the Body

Introduction

Almost all living organisms are made up of a number of subunits known as cells. In the animal kingdom the smallest creatures, the protozoa, consist of a single cell only. In more complex creatures there are very large numbers of cells; a mammal may possess billions on billions of these subunits within its body. If you could count the number of red blood cells in a small drop of blood oozing from a finger prick, you would probably find about a hundred million of them.

We can study the control of the activity of living animals at three levels. The first is the control of biochemical reactions within the cell walls. At this level is governed the building up of useful substances and the breaking down of unwanted ones. The balance between these processes is one of the factors influencing the rate of growth of the cell. In recent years, biochemists have begun to make exciting discoveries about the control of reactions by the genetic material contained in the chromosomes. Many forms of cancer may be due to a breakdown in this control system. The cells grow and divide much more rapidly than usual and produce a dangerous malignant growth.

The second level which we can look at is that of the communication between the various cells contained within a single organism. In the protozoa, the single unit carries out all the functions essential for life. In more complex animals, the cells become more and more specialized. You may have heard the cynical but accurate saying that specialization is knowing more and more about less and less. A cell in a more highly developed animal cannot perform nearly as many functions as a protozoan can; it does perform its more limited tasks more efficiently. Some cells become specialized for digesting food, some for moving the animal along, some for building a skeleton to support the animal, some for collecting information about the animal's surroundings. There are cells which are specialized to perform every conceivable living activity; without this specialization, a highly complex organism would be impossible.

If a unit made up of a number of small subunits is to work efficiently, you can no doubt see that there must be some means of passing information between these subunits and of directing their activity. Any president or prime minister who hopes to govern his country well must have an organization under him which is made up of at least three components. He must have a system for collecting as much information as possible about the country and its inhabitants. He must have a system in which this vast mass of information is analyzed and sifted so that only the most important items are presented to him for his consideration. Lastly, when he has studied the information and decided on a course of action, he must have an effective organization for putting his decisions into effect. If he had no system for collecting information, his decisions as to courses of action might be quite unrelated to the needs of the nation. If he had no system for analyzing and sifting this information, he would be hopelessly overworked. If he had no organization to ensure that his decisions were acted on, he would be a president in name only and not in reality. Similarly, in a single animal there must be a means of collecting information about the state of activity of all the cells in the body, of coordinating this knowledge, and of directing any changes which may be necessary. This task is carried out by the nervous and endocrine systems.

The third level of organization is in many ways an extension of the second and is the means by which whole individuals communicate with one another. Consider an admiral who is about to direct his fleet into battle against the enemy. Like the president just discussed he must have a system for collecting information about his own fleet and a system for directing those under his command. But if he is to have any success he must also be able to obtain information about the disposition of the enemy's ships and must have at his disposal weapons which he can use against his opponent. On one level, he is concerned with the relationship of the various ships of his own fleet to one another. On another level, he is concerned with the relationship of his whole fleet to that of the enemy.

Similarly an animal must have organs for collecting information about the outside world and organs for collecting information about the state of its own body. Ultimately, no matter how complex the electronic aids may be, communication between human beings depends on our ability to use our special senses, particularly vision and hearing, for receiving information from outside. The process of giving information to others depends largely on the ability of our brain to direct the activity of certain muscles in the arm and hand and in the larynx and mouth. You can clearly see that this third level is merely an extension of the second.

In this book, we shall not be concerned with the first level of organization—the control of intracellular biochemical activity. We shall be concerned with the second and third levels. We shall learn how information is collected, both about the world around us and about the activity of cells and organs within our bodies. We shall see something of the way in which this information is processed and, finally, how the decisions reached are put into effect.

2: How the Nervous System Evolved

In a primitive tribe, with only a small number of people, ordinary speech may be a satisfactory means of communication. Any news rapidly spreads through the whole group. If a young man kills a buffalo, he tells those nearest to him; they pass on the information to others, and before long the whole tribe knows. It is rather like gossip among the ladies of a city suburb. Once one of them has uncovered a scandal they all very soon learn of it. But ordinary speech can only be a satisfactory means of communicating when a group is very small and closely knit. As a community becomes larger it is impossible to pass on information satisfactorily by simply talking face to face; other methods must be devised. Suppose a doctor wanted to consult a colleague on the other side of a city. He could go out into the street and ask some passer-by to take the message and pass it on. The message might eventually reach the other side of the city but, on the other hand, it might not. In any case, it would be a very slow process, and it is very doubtful whether the message which arrived would be the same as the one passed on by the first doctor. You may possibly have heard the story of a British Army officer in the front lines who sent a verbal request back to his general: "Send reinforcements, I'm going to advance." The general was surprised and not a little angry to receive the message: "Send three and fourpence, I'm going to a dance." You can see that ordinary speech has two great disadvantages for transmitting information over long distances. It is slow, and the message very easily becomes distorted. Other methods, such as the telephone, must be used. Two people, many miles apart, can be connected directly and a message can pass rapidly between them without distortion.

Similarly, in a very simple animal containing only a few cells, a change in the state of one cell might be passed on directly to its neighbors. For instance, one cell might take in food and the products of digestion might then slowly pass outward to others and eventually diffuse throughout the animal. This would always be an unsatisfactory process, and in an animal body consisting of a very large number of cells it would be quite useless. There must be a completely new method of passing information from one region of the body to another. If an animal is to survive in a hostile world, it must have a way of rapidly carrying the news of an attack on one region to the rest of the body. On the other hand, if favorable conditions are encountered by one cell the news must be quickly spread so that the whole animal can take advantage of the situation. To meet these needs the structure known as the neuron came into being. We must spend a little time in trying to understand how it works.

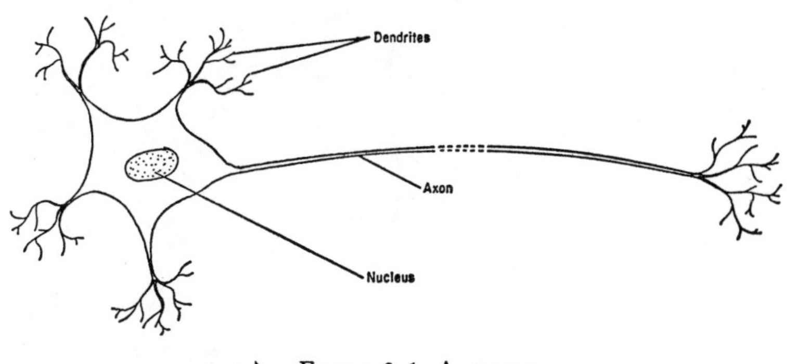

▶ FIGURE 2–1. A neuron.

A neuron is a cell which can be activated by a change occurring in one part of it. This activation produces a nerve impulse which can travel very rapidly over the surface of the neuron. On reaching the other end of the cell the impulse can produce a further activation, either of another neuron which carries the impulse still further afield or of some effector structure such as a muscle or gland cell. If a neuron were long and thin, it could carry impulses between the two rapidly and without distortion. In this book we shall see how the elaboration of this simple principle has led to the development of a complex nervous system.

HYDRA

We find the simplest neurons in the coelenterates. That is rather a large word for a group of small animals which includes the sea anemones, the corals, and the jellyfish. A very simple coelenterate, called hydra, is common in fresh water. In it there are two layers of cells, one lining a cavity and the other facing the outside

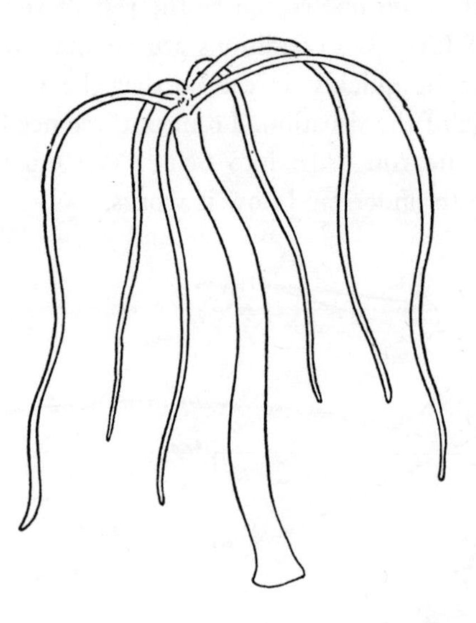

▶ FIGURE 2–2. Hydra in the expanded state.

world. Between the two is a jellylike substance known as the mesogloea. If you saw an active hydra, it would look like a slender column with tentacles, which are used to catch food, waving from the top. When inactive the animal is simply a small blob of contracted tissue. In both the outer and the inner layers there are special sensory cells. These cells are prolonged into hairs which project away from the mesogloea; the internal cells project into the cavity and the external ones onto the outside world. The hairs are particularly sensitive to mechanical disturbances. They can detect a current of water or a small animal moving over the surface of the hydra. The part of the sensory cell next to the mesogloea is also prolonged into a process. This links up with a nerve net, and information about a change at the surface of the animal can be passed into the nerve net in the form of an impulse.

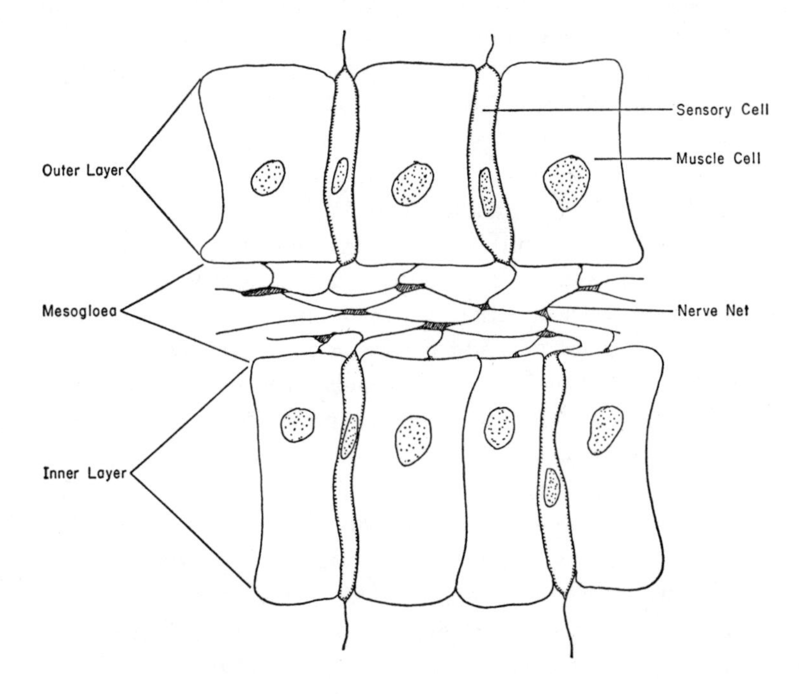

▶ FIGURE 2–3. Cell detail of hydra.

There are two nerve nets, one on each side of the mesogloea. They are joined by strands of nervous tissue and so information can be passed from one part of the body to any other part.

The nerve net is very aptly named: it really does look like a net. The neurons each consist of a nucleated cell body, and their cytoplasm is drawn out into several fine processes. These processes link up with the processes from other cell bodies, thus making a network. People used to think that the neurons were not completely separate but were linked by protoplasmic bridges, making a system without true gaps. It is now known that in hydra, just as in higher animals, each neuron is a separate unit. The processes of one neuron make very close contact with the next neuron but the two cells do not actually fuse. The small gap between the two neurons is called a synapse. In coelenterates it is not known how a nervous impulse crosses a synapse; in higher animals when an impulse reaches the end of a nerve it causes a chemical to be released. In turn, this generates an impulse in the next neuron. The discovery of this mechanism forms an exciting chapter in the history of neurophysiology (see chapters 12 and 15).

If you were to touch a sensory hair of a hydra with a pointer, the cell would discharge an impulse into the nerve net. The nerve processes in this animal can conduct activity in either direction, and a synapse can also pass an impulse from one neuron to another in either direction. When an impulse reaches a synapse it meets with resistance, and it may or may not pass on to the next neuron. The arrival of one impulse at a synapse, even if it does not cross it, seems to lower the resistance to the next impulse if the second one falls within a certain limited period of time. You can see that a single impulse will probably not get far in the nerve net. A short train of impulses will get farther, because the early ones lower the synaptic resistance for the later ones. A prolonged series may be able to spread over the whole network. In hydra, a light stimulus to a sensory cell may only cause one or two impulses to be generated, and the activity will not spread far. A strong stimulus, however, will produce a stream of impulses. The activity will spread over the nerve net in all directions; if the stimulus is strong enough, it will reach every part of the animal.

There are several essential facts about the nerve net that are important for us to understand. Because both the nerve processes and the synapses can conduct an impulse in either direction, activity will radiate outward from the point of stimulus in all directions. The fact that the synapses are resistant to the transmission of an impulse, but that this resistance can be overcome by a succession of impulses, means that the area of the nerve net over which the activity spreads will be proportional to the strength of the stimulus. A light stimulus will produce impulses which spread over a small area; a strong stimulus may involve the whole animal. An impulse only travels along a process relatively slowly. Many people imagine that a nerve acts simply as a wire and that the impulse is conducted at the speed of electricity. Conduction is in fact much more complex and much slower than this (see Chapter 3). Each time a synapse is reached there is yet another delay. You can see that a nerve net is not a particularly efficient form of nervous system. The processes from the cell bodies are not very long, and an impulse must cross synapse after synapse. This takes a lot of time, and information can only pass relatively slowly from one part of the animal to another.

If the nerve net of hydra only received information from the sensory cells and did not pass it on to cells designed to act on the information, it would be quite useless. There is no point in having a system for collecting information unless it is possible to put the knowledge which is gained to some use. In fact, the nerve net links up with the muscle cells which make up most of the body of hydra. These cells have a number of jobs to do, but one of their most important properties is their ability to contract when they receive an impulse from the nerve net. This ability would be wasted unless a whole group of cells could contract together. In rowing, a good crew wins because they all put in their oars and pull at precisely the same time. The boat shoots forward, and when all the oars are removed from the water at one time, the boat glides on with nothing to check its course. If the members of the crew put their oars in the water at random, some would be pulling while others were coming forward for the next stroke. Chaos would result, and the boat would move slowly. Similarly, in hydra a group of cells must contract together, since one acting alone would have a negligible effect. The activity of a crew is coordinated because all the crew members carefully follow stroke. The activity of the muscle cells is coordinated because they all receive impulses from the nerve net. Without this nervous system the muscle cells would be of very little use to hydra. With it they are of the utmost importance.

Scattered among the cells in the tentacles of hydra are many structures known as cnidoblasts. These are hydra's automatic weapons; they are not connected with the nerve net, but fire when a small hair sticking out from the cnidoblast is touched. They are of several different sorts: some send out a sharp point which discharges poison, some release a sticky material, and some send out coils which can wrap around hairs and bristles. Suppose we watch while a small creature bumps against a tentacle. The cnidoblasts fire. The unfortunate animal is fastened to the tentacle by glue, held on by coils wrapped firmly around any hairs or bristles, and pierced by poisoned darts. To make sure that the job is finished, neighboring tentacles, thanks to a coordinated contraction of the muscle cells, bend over and, as they touch the prey, their cnidoblasts are discharged. Finally, we see the tentacles bend back and deliver the food to the mouth. Once inside the cavity of the animal it would be digested by juices released by the cells of the inner layer. All the coordinated movements essential for obtaining food would be quite impossible without a sensory system for detecting the presence of the prey and a nerve net for conducting this information to other regions of hydra and coordinating the activity of the muscle cells.

Just as this system of sensory receptor, nerve, and effector organ is vital in attack, so it is in defense. If an expanded hydra, with its tentacles freely moving in the water, suddenly receives a sharp pinprick, it will rapidly contract to a small blob of protoplasm which bears no apparent relation to the elegant creature of a moment before. This sharp stimulus generates a stream of impulses which clearly passes to all regions of the body. There is a coordinated contraction of the muscle cells, the tentacles are drawn in, and the body contracts down. The coordinated mechanism has made the animal much less vulnerable to attack from outside.

The primitive nerve net of hydra is theoretically important to us for it is a possible stage on the road of nervous evolution traveled by higher organisms. It is also, of course, of immense practical value to hydra itself. However, for higher animals, such as ourselves, such a structure would have a number of disadvantages. In a network, impulses have frequently to cross synapses and this obviously means that the spread of information is a relatively slow procedure. This may not matter very much in a tiny animal like hydra but in one the size of man it would be a very serious handicap. In hydra there do not appear to be neurons with very long processes which could transmit impulses over great distances without interruption. The nerve net is also very generalized in function. Since the whole net can carry out a multiplicity of functions none of these is very highly developed. For instance, synaptic transmission might be faster if the synapse were specialized to conduct impluses only in one direction as it is in the mammals. Since the nerve net is so constructed that it is essential for synapses to conduct in both directions, this sort of specialization is impossible, and transmission is slow.

In some of the sea anemones the first improvement in the system can be found. The sea anemones are closely related to hydra. They are much larger, however, with a fat central column and short fat tentacles around the mouth. Arranged around the column and traveling from the mouth of the animal toward its base are several specialized neurons. Their processes are about a third of an inch long and deserve to be given the name axon, which is used for the long processes of higher nerve cells. These axons are much longer than any of the ordinary processes in the nerve net. Using these neurons an impulse can travel over relatively enormous distances without having to cross a synapse. Information can be carried quickly from one end of the animal to the other. Thanks to these long axons any unpleasant stimulus applied to the anemone produces an exceedingly rapid contraction. Avoiding action can be taken much more quickly than if the animal had only a simple nerve net.

THE MEDUSA

While one branch of the coelenterate group remains firmly attached to the bottom, another branch has a form which floats through the sea. In many species the two forms alternate during the life cycle. The floating forms are called medusae. They are circular in shape and often transparent, the familiar jellyfish being a good example. The medusa is convex upward, and it swims by

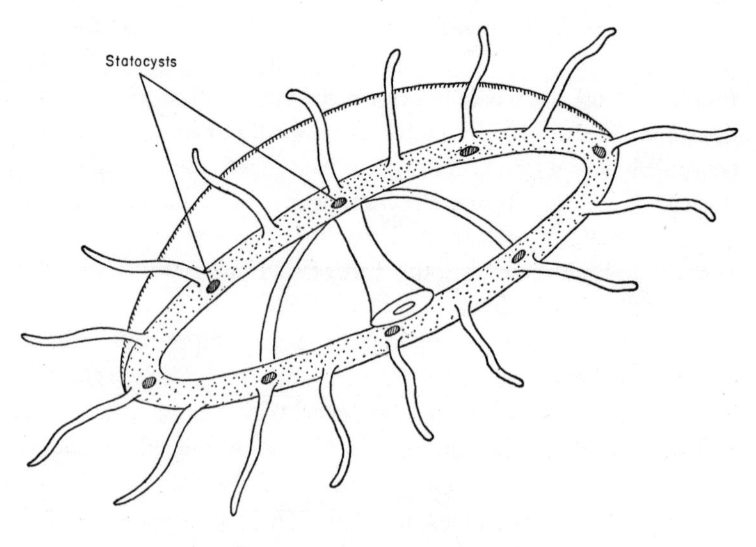

▶ FIGURE 2–4. A typical medusa.

pulling its edges inward and creating a downcurrent of water; this pushes the animal upward. The medusa has a very ingenious system for keeping it on an even keel while it is swimming. It has receptors which are designed to detect any tilting of the animal and a well-organized tract of nervous tissue to carry the information to the appropriate muscle cells—the ones on the side of the medusa which is tilting downward. These cells contract more vigorously, there is a stronger downcurrent of water on that side, and the animal is forced on to an even keel again. The receptors which detect the tilting are known as statocysts and are situated around the edge of the medusa. They are rather like the plumb lines used in building a brick wall to detect variations from the vertical. Each consists of a tiny cavity. Suspended by a hair from the roof of this cavity is a speck of calcium carbonate, known as a statolith. When the medusa is level the statolith hangs free in the middle of the cavity. When the medusa tilts the statolith bumps against the wall. If the medusa tilts to one side the statoliths on that side will bump against the outer walls of

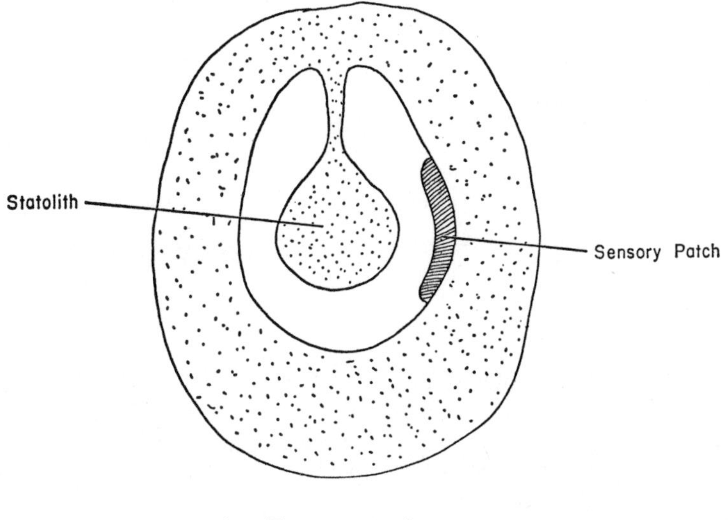

▶ FIGURE 2–5. A statocyst.

their cavities. Those on the opposite side will bump against the inner walls. Now each statocyst is constructed so that on the outer wall, but nowhere else, there is a group of highly sensitive cells. When the medusa tilts to one side the statoliths on that side, but not in any other region, will bump against this sensory patch. A

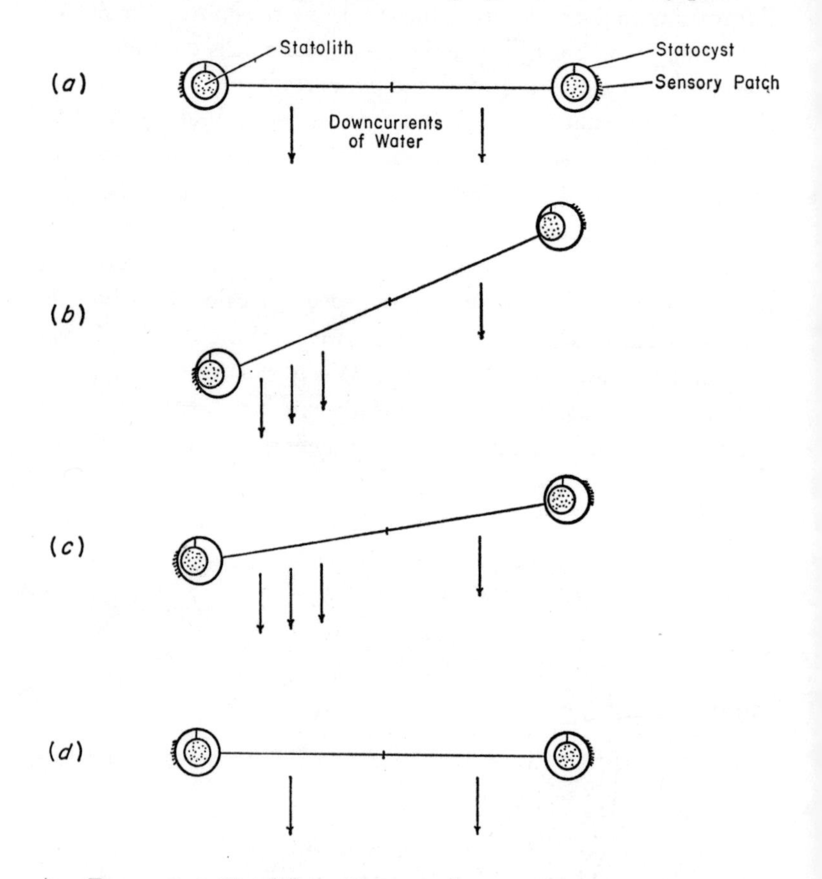

▶ FIGURE 2–6. Simplified diagram of statocysts in action (*a*) The medusa is on an even keel with the statoliths hanging free. (*b*) The medusa tilts to the left and the statolith on that side bumps against the sensory patch. This causes impulses to be sent to the swimming muscles on that side. The muscles contract and the downcurrents of water there are increased. (*c*) and (*d*). The medusa returns to an even keel.

stream of impulses will be generated and will pass to the muscle cells on that side. These will contract more vigorously, producing a stronger downcurrent of water and will restore the medusa to an even keel. No matter which way the animal tilts the mechanism is designed to produce a stronger contraction of the swimming muscles of that side. It is our first real example of a section of a nervous system specialized to perform a particular function.

THE CENTRAL NERVOUS SYSTEM

Despite this, even in the most advanced coelenterates we can find little evidence of a nervous center which coordinates and directs the activity of the animal as a whole. No particular section of the nervous system receives the information from all the sense organs, assesses its value, and accordingly directs the operation of effector mechanisms. This type of centralization does not occur in animals which have radial symmetry. It only makes its appearance when bilateral symmetry is developed. Radially symmetrical animals have upper and lower ends but not front and rear ones. If you were looking down on such a creature and were asked to cut it into two similar halves there are a whole series of possible cuts which you could make. This could not be done with animals possessing bilateral symmetry. They have front and rear ends as well as upper and lower sides. On looking down at such an animal there is only one possible cut which you could make if you wanted to divide the animal into two equal parts. This cut must pass in the mid-line from the front of the animal to the back. Any other cut would produce two different parts.

If an animal like a jellyfish moves, no particular part of the animal always leads the way. At one time one side may go first, at another time another. When a bilaterally symmetrical animal, such as a worm, moves, its front end will almost always lead the way. You do not often see a worm going backward or sideways. Since the front part will be the first region to encounter new situations, it seems natural that the head should possess a richer sensory innervation than other parts of the body. There will clearly be an

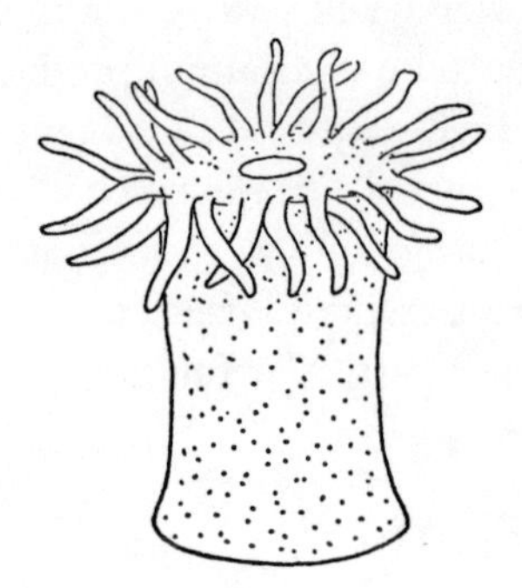

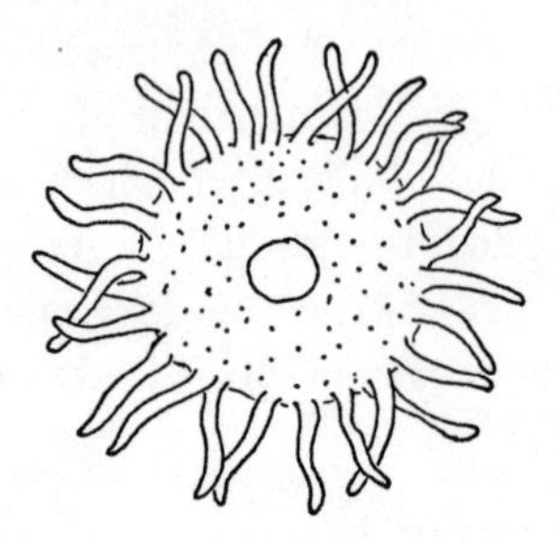

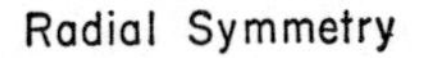

▶ FIGURE 2–7. Animals with radial and bilateral symmetry.

advantage if the special senses are highly developed there so that they can detect new stimuli as soon as possible. Because of this there will be a large concentration of sensory structures in the head. If the information received by this battery of sensory receptors is to be useful, it must be conveyed as rapidly as possible to such effector organs as the muscles and glands, which are not concentrated in the head but distributed throughout the body. In order to pass information to these effectors long, uninterrupted tracts of nervous tissue must be developed. This is the beginning of the spinal cord.

Much of the information which is received does not require any action to be taken. For instance, all day we are subjected to a continual background of noise but this does not lead to any action. A system must be developed which sifts out this irrelevant information and prevents it from passing to the effectors. It seems logical that a processing mechanism should be developed right at the anterior end of the animal. The first signs of this development are seen in the worms, where there is a tiny agglomeration of nervous tissue which probably performs this sort of function. Brain is far too grandiose a term for it but, nevertheless, in it lie the seeds of the structure which has enabled man to rise to the dominant position on this earth.

All but the most primitive animal groups have their bodies arranged in a segmented manner. This is most obvious in such animals as the earthworm where you can readily see the segments on the surface. The segmentation of the animal as a whole has its counterpart in the nervous system. In the earthworm there is a slight swelling of the nerve cord in each segment. Into this swelling pass fibers from the sensory receptors in that segment; out of it pass the motor fibers to such effector structures of that segment as the muscles. In higher animals this division of the body tends to be obliterated but that of the nervous system remains, even in man. In the neck and below, pairs of nerves are given off from the spinal cord at regular intervals. Each pair corresponds to one of the primitive body segments. In a peripheral nerve, the sensory and motor fibers are all mixed up together, but just before the nerve reaches the spinal cord there is an astonishing sorting-out. The nerve divides into two roots. All the sensory fibers enter the back of the spinal cord. This is the way by which information enters the central nervous system. All the motor fibers carrying instructions for the muscles emerge from the front of the cord.

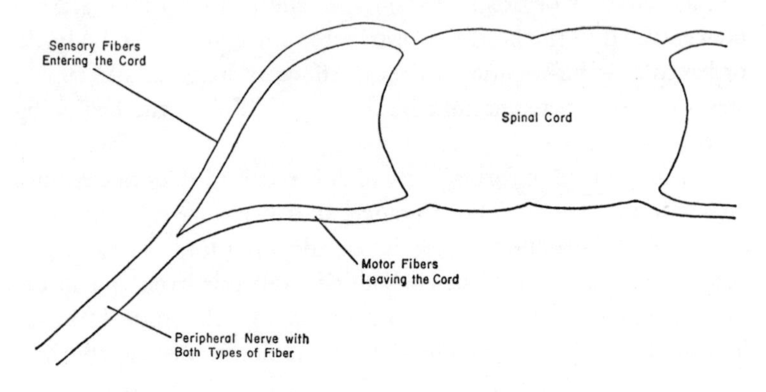

▶ FIGURE 2–8. The spinal cord with its two roots.

Because of this arrangement we can stimulate or record from a section of nerve made up entirely either of sensory or of motor fibers. But for this, the advance of neurophysiology would have been much hindered because of the difficulty of separating out sensory or motor fibers from a mixed peripheral nerve.

It would be most interesting for us to work up through the animal kingdom looking at the improvements apparent in the nervous organization of each group. We should see a greater and greater tendency for a mass of tissue to be concentrated at the head end. This plays a more and more important part in the life of the animal. It collects more information, assesses its relevance more capably, and directs action more effectively. But this increasing development of the brain would be meaningless without a parallel improvement in other structures. More sensitive receptors to distinguish between a host of types of stimulus, more efficient effector organs to carry out more capably the instructions from the brain, more rapid conduction mechanisms to carry news quickly from one end of a large animal to another, more efficient synaptic processes—all these are vital. Yet even in lowly forms of life we have been able to see the basic essentials for a communications system. These are a means of collecting information about the animal's internal organs and about the outside world, a means of sifting this information to eliminate the unimportant, and a means of passing on the vital knowledge to effector structures. The study of these three necessities will form the theme for those parts of this book which are concerned with communication by the nervous system.

3 Nerve Cells and Their Messages

When lying on the sand beside the sea, with your eyes closed and delightful dreams passing through your mind, you do not expect some unkind friend to come and stick a pin into your toe. If this did happen your reaction would be rapid. Without thinking about it you would at once withdraw your foot. This is really rather remarkable.

The information about the pin was collected by a receptor in your toe and passed to the central nervous system by a sensory nerve fiber. This fiber is probably more than 4 feet long from its ending in the toe to its first synapse at the lower end of the brain, yet in diameter it would only be about 10 μ. You are probably unfamiliar with this unit of length: 1 μ is one-thousandth part of a millimeter. Perhaps it can be made clearer if you imagine the sensory nerve fiber to be 2,500 times its actual size. Its diameter would then be about 1 inch and in a tall person its length would be over 2 miles. By using a delicate instrument to measure changes in potential we can record the electrical disturbance which passes along a nerve fiber. Electrodes for picking up the disturbances can be placed on the nerve and the potential changes magnified and observed on the screen of a cathode-ray oscilloscope. If we use two sets of electrodes, one near the toe and one near the spinal cord, we can learn a great deal about a nerve impulse by studying it as it passes each of these.

If we were to do this, two striking facts would emerge. We should see that the size of the electrical change near the spinal cord was just as great as that recorded in the toe; the nerve impulse does not alter in magnitude as it passes along the fiber. In addition, there would be a clear and comparatively large time lag between the two readings. The impulse takes a finite time to pass from the toe to the cord. By measuring the length of nerve fiber between the two sets of electrodes and the time the impulse takes to pass from one to the other, we could measure the speed of conduction. In a mammalian nerve it might be about 300 feet per second.

These two facts mean that the impulse cannot travel by simple electrical means. The nerve fiber cannot behave like a wire which merely conducts electricity from one end to the other. If it did, the records would be different in two ways. The speed of conduction would be much higher, about 186,000 miles per second. Because of the way in which such a very long, very thin conductor would resist the passage of electricity, the disturbance recorded would be much smaller near the spinal cord than it would in the foot. Since the impulse at both places is the same size, you can clearly see that, while electricity must play some part in nervous conduction, the nerve fiber does not behave like a simple wire.

In any theory of nerve conduction we must explain how an impulse of constant size is conducted. Why is there no fading off in intensity as it passes along the fiber? There are two possibilities for the source of the energy which keeps the impulse going. It might come from the original mechanical stimulus or it might come from the nerve itself. The fact that it is possible to detect very light touches from a hair or a feather makes the first of these ideas unlikely. It is difficult to imagine how the lightest possible touch that we can feel could have enough energy by itself to send an impulse to the spinal cord. We are forced to the conclusion that the energy must come from the nerve itself. A neat experiment can help to show this. We can cool a small length of nerve and measure the size of the impulse and the conduction velocity in this small section as opposed to the rest of the fiber. As the impulse comes along, when it enters the cooled section it suddenly becomes smaller and travels more slowly. Once it has passed through this section, however, it regains its former height and velocity. This means that the properties of the nerve impulse depend more on the state of the nerve than on the way in which the impulse is generated. An analogy may help to make this clearer. Suppose we have two lengths of railway track, one which is electrified and the other which is not, and that on each of these tracks there is an engine. Each engine can be set in motion by giving it a push; in the case of the engine on the electrified track this throws a switch which sets off an electric motor. Suppose that we give each engine a push of the same size. The engine on the ordinary track will travel quickly at first but will soon slow down and stop; the only energy available to keep it going came from the original push. This is similar to the idea that the nerve impulse energy comes from the original stimulus. On the other hand, with the electric engine, the push which sets it in motion also throws the switch which enables it to get energy from the track. The speed of the engine will depend on the power available. In a section of track where the electrical power is low the engine will slow down; as soon as it enters a normal track section it will speed up again. This second case is obviously much closer to the way in which a nerve behaves than the first one is. In a nerve the tiny amount of energy from the stimulus seems to trigger off another process; once this has happened the energy for impulse conduction comes from the nerve itself.

THE RESTING MEMBRANE POTENTIAL

In this chapter we are mainly interested in what goes on in the elongated part of the fiber known as the axon. We are not concerned with the triggering-off of the impulse, but in the way in which the initiated impulse travels. Essentially the axon consists of a cylindrical membrane separating two solutions. One, inside the axon, is the intracellular fluid; the other is the tissue fluid surrounding the axon. The composition of these two solutions is very different. Their ionic content is particularly important in nerve conduction. Outside the axon the concentration of sodium ions is very high, that of potassium ions very low; inside these concentrations are reversed. Outside the chief negative ion is chloride; inside there is little chloride, and the negative component is made up mainly by organic ions.

Consider now in general terms some of the consequences of this. Whenever two solutions containing different concentrations of a particular ion are in contact, a potential difference is developed between the two (the solutions must clearly not be in such free contact that rapid diffusion takes place and allows the concentrations on the two sides to become equal). We can easily demonstrate this by using two salt solutions of differing strengths and linking them by a bridge containing colloidal material. The colloidal material allows ions to migrate, but not very freely, across the bridge. A potential difference which can be measured by a voltmeter immediately develops between the two solutions. Nernst showed theoretically that provided the two ionic concentrations are known, the potential difference that will be produced can be easily calculated from the following equation (K is a constant).

$$\text{Potential} = K \log \left(\frac{\text{concentration on one side}}{\text{concentration on the other}} \right)$$

If the two concentrations are equal the expression on the far right will be 1. The logarithm of 1 is 0 and obviously no potential difference will be developed. The larger the concentration difference, the bigger will be the potential difference produced.

Another analogy may help to make this idea clear. Imagine a tray which contains a large number of marbles, all of the same size. The tray is divided into two equal compartments by a partition, and in this partition are holes through which these marbles can pass. To start with, suppose that there is an equal number of marbles on each side of the partition. If we pick up the tray and shake it evenly, some marbles from the right-hand side will go through to the left and some from the left-hand side will pass in the opposite direction. Because there is an equal number of marbles on each side, approximately an equal number will pass in each direction; the sum of these two movements will be 0, and there will still be an equal number of marbles on each side. Any tendency of the marbles to move in one direction is counteracted by an equal and opposite tendency for them to move in the other direction. There is no net migration. If the marbles were ions, and the partition were a membrane, we should say that the potential difference developed was 0. The expression on the far right of the Nernst equation would be equal to 1.

Now consider the situation in which all the marbles are on the right side to start with. When the tray is shaken, there will be a tendency for marbles to move from right to left, but, at least to start with, there can be no movement in the opposite direction. Again, if the marbles were ions, we should say that the difference in their number on the two sides had produced a potential difference. The size of the potential difference will depend on the ratio of the concentrations on the two sides. The two examples we have considered are the extremes. Usually, the situation will be somewhere in between. It should perhaps be pointed out that, if the partition had no holes, no marbles would pass from one side to the other, no matter what the difference in numbers was; no potential difference would be produced.

We must now apply all this to the axon itself. The cylindrical membrane is equivalent to the partition of the analogy. It is possible to measure the ionic concentrations inside and outside this membrane. There follows a typical list of concentrations for the giant axon of the squid. The units are millimoles per kilo of water, but do not worry about what this means. All you need to understand here is that there is much more potassium inside the fiber than there is in the surrounding fluid; with sodium and chloride, the situation is reversed.

	INSIDE	OUTSIDE
Potassium	360	22
Sodium	50	440
Chloride	80	560

Suppose for a moment that only potassium ions could pass through the membrane. The relative concentrations of these ions, inside and outside the fiber, would then determine the membrane potential. We could use the figures to calculate, by means of the Nernst equation, what this potential would be. If we did this we should find that, in this case, the inside of the axon would be about 90 millivolts (mV) negative to the surrounding fluid. On the other hand, if only sodium could pass through the membrane, the inside would be about 50 mV positive to the surrounding fluid. You may wonder why I have chosen this rather strange squid nerve as an example. It is because this particular axon is one of the largest known and it is comparatively easy to insert a microelectrode into it. Little damage seems to be caused and the nerve behaves relatively normally. Investigations on other fibers suggest that they all behave in a similar way.

Suppose that we have a fine glass microelectrode connected to an apparatus for measuring the potential difference between the tip of the microelectrode and the surrounding tissues. When the tip is in the extracellular fluid around a nerve this difference will be 0. If we then push the electrode against the squid axon until it pierces the membrane there will be a remarkable change. As the fiber is pierced we shall see the potential recording, which had been 0, suddenly become about 70 mV negative. The inside of the fiber is clearly negative to the outside. This potential difference is close to the theoretical potential difference which we would expect if only potassium ions could pass through the membrane. Sodium does not seem to be able to cross the membrane since, if it could, the inside of the fiber would be more positive.

How can we test this? It is really quite simple. If the membrane is permeable to potassium, varying the concentration of potassium ions in the external fluid will produce variations in the membrane potential. By making the external potassium concentration equal to that inside it should be possible to abolish the membrane potential altogether. On the other hand, if sodium ions cannot pass through the membrane, varying the external sodium concentration will have no effect on the resting membrane potential. These experiments have been done, and it has been shown that the membrane of the nerve fiber behaves as though it were only permeable to potassium ions. Very delicate experiments show that sodium and chloride may play a small part in determining the resting membrane potential. For our purposes here, however, we may consider it to be negligible. If we consider the situation with sodium and potassium in terms of our marble analogy, it may be made clear. Suppose the potassium ions, which are small, are represented by small marbles and the sodium ions, which are large, by large ones. Most of the small marbles will be on the right-hand side, representing the inside of the fiber, while the large ones will be on the left side, representing the outside. The partition has a few small holes through which the small marbles can pass but there are no large holes; consequently the big marbles cannot pass from one side to the other. If we vary the number of small marbles on the two sides we vary the number which can pass through the partition. If the marbles were ions we would say that we had altered the potential difference between the two sides. No matter how much the number of the large marbles is varied, it will not alter the number of marbles which pass from one side to the other. If the large marbles were the sodium ions, they would not alter the potential difference between the two sides.

THE ACTION POTENTIAL

This is all very well for a fiber which is at rest. But a nerve fiber is designed to conduct nervous impulses; what happens under these conditions? Again we can record the changes in the membrane potential which take place, this time when an impulse passes by. The changes are dramatic. Not only does the membrane potential alter, but the inside of the fiber actually becomes markedly positive to the outside. From theoretical considerations, the only possible ion which could produce a change of this sort would be sodium. It is as though the membrane, impermeable at rest to sodium, suddenly becomes much more permeable to it than to any other ion. For a fleeting moment the membrane behaves as though its potential were entirely governed by sodium. Once again we can test these possibilities by varying the concentrations of ions in the external fluid and observing their effect on the action potential (as the change in potential when an impulse passes is called). Within limits, varying the concentration of potassium has little effect on the magnitude of the action potential. If the external concentration is raised too much, however, and the resting potential approaches zero, the fiber becomes inexcitable. This seems to be a secondary consequence of altering the resting potential rather than a direct effect on the action potential. On the other hand, if we vary the sodium concentration we produce a very different situation. There is no effect on the resting potential but the action potential is markedly altered. When the external sodium is reduced to between a third and a sixth of its normal level, the action potential no longer becomes positive. If we replace the external fluid by a solution containing no sodium, no action potential can be produced. The axon will not conduct impulses at all. The action potential seems to depend entirely on the presence of sodium in the external fluid.

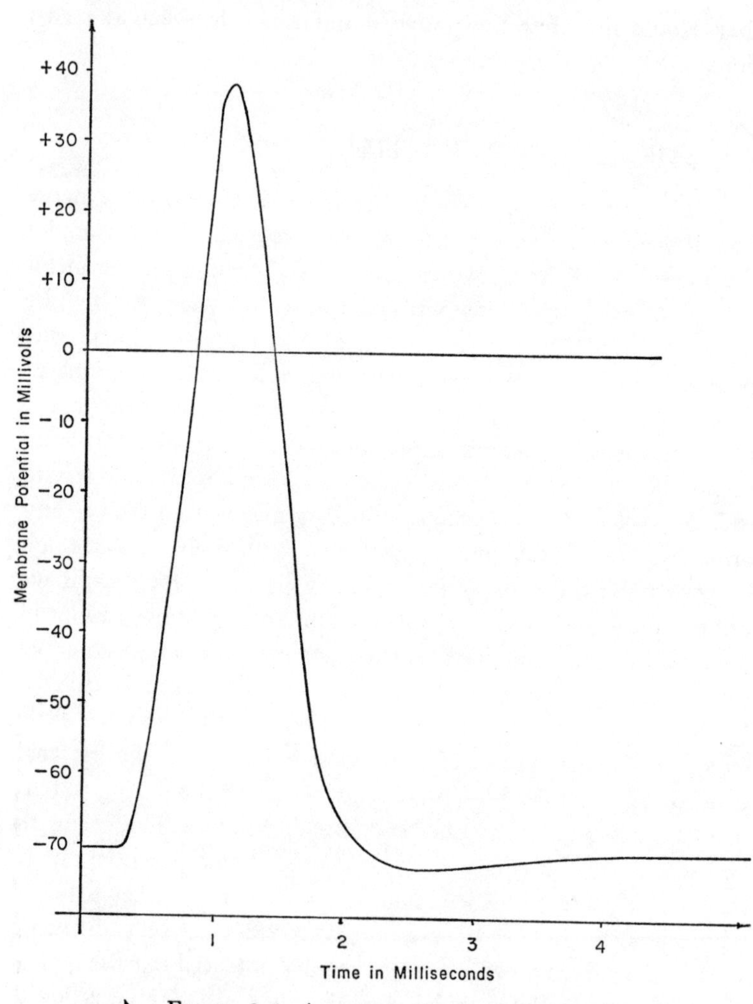

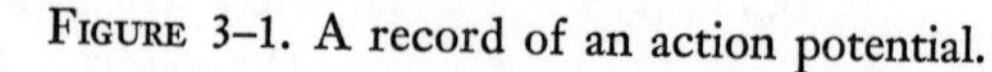
FIGURE 3–1. A record of an action potential.

Again returning to our marble analogy, it is as though there were a sudden change in the partition. Previously the large marbles were unable to pass through and the tendency of marbles to move from one side to the other was determined by the small ones. Suddenly a great many large holes appear in the partition.

Now the big marbles can pass through the partition in large numbers. Equally suddenly the large holes vanish and the partition returns to normal. For a brief moment the pattern of the passage of marbles has been determined by the large ones. For a brief moment the axon membrane becomes permeable to the large sodium ions. They rush into the fiber and the membrane potential becomes positive.

You are no doubt wondering by now how the impulse

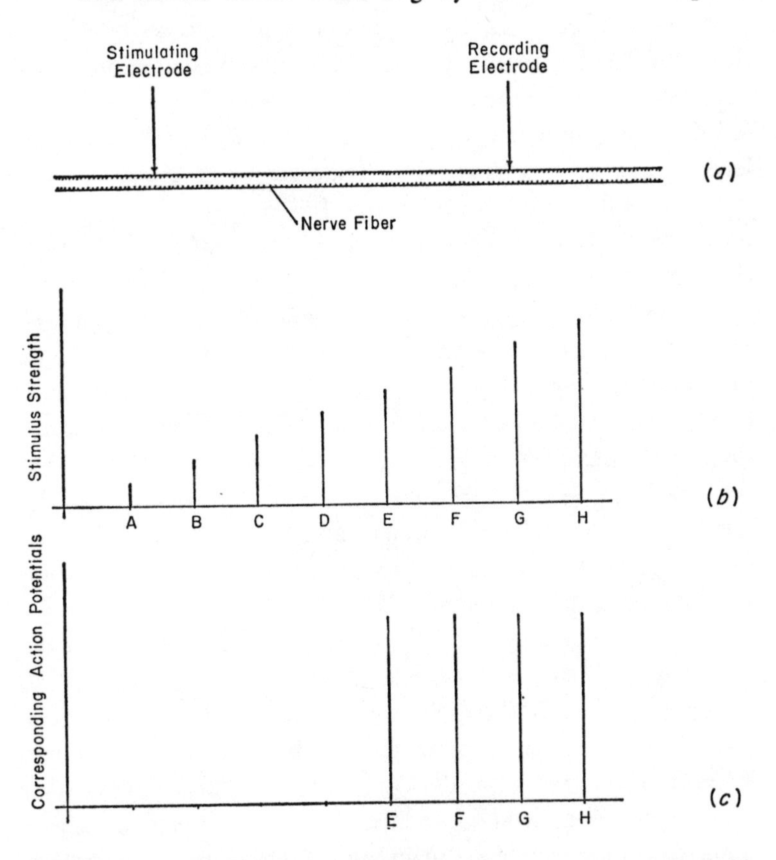

▶ FIGURE 3–2. An experiment to illustrate the concept of threshold. (*a*) The experimental set-up. (*b*) Records of the stimulus strengths. (*c*) The action potentials which result.

begins. We can study the initiation of the action potential by stimulating the nerve with an electric shock at one point and recording at another point any impulses which may be produced. At very low levels of stimulus no impulse is generated. The stimulus intensity can be increased gradually until suddenly at one particular level a full action potential is produced. At one level of stimulation there is no impulse; at the next, slightly higher level, the impulse is fully developed. No matter how much bigger the electric shock becomes, the impulse will increase no further in size. The shock intensity which first causes the initiation of an impulse is known as the threshold. At all levels below the threshold no action potential is produced. Just at threshold and at all levels above it, in a single fiber under constant conditions the action potential remains the same size. It is known as an all-or-none phenomenon. It is either not present, or is present fully developed; there are no halfway stages.

The picture just described is obtained if the single nerve fiber is stimulated at one point and the impulse is recorded some way along the fiber. If it were possible to record the intracellular changes which take place at the point where the shock actually fires off the impulse, we should see something rather different. At low levels of shock there would be a small reduction in the potential difference between inside and outside (the resting membrane potential). As the stimulus intensity increased, this reduction would become greater and greater until suddenly at the threshold, when the membrane potential was reduced to somewhere in the region of −30 to −50 mV, an impulse would be produced. Changes below this threshold level cannot produce a sufficient alteration in the membrane to allow sodium to rush in. Changes above this level so alter the properties of the membrane that sodium can rush in and produce the action potential. Almost immediately the membrane again becomes impermeable to sodium. We know comparatively little about this momentary increase in sodium permeability. Possibly the electric shock causes some rearrangement of the structure of the membrane, allowing sodium to pour in.

Once such an impulse has been started, it will continue to travel over the surface of the membrane. If one region of an electrical conducting system is positive to another, current will flow from the positive to the negative part, so tending to reduce the potential difference between the two. When an action potential fires off, the inside of the active region for a moment becomes positive to the regions on each side. Local electric currents will flow from the positive to the negative regions. The latter will therefore be made less negative with reference to the outside of the fiber. The resting potential may be altered sufficiently to bring

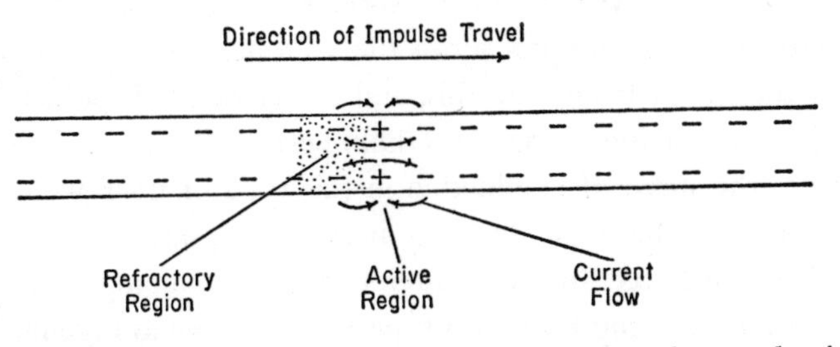

▶ FIGURE 3–3. The local circuits involved in impulse conduction.

the membrane in the adjacent inactive region to the threshold value, thus firing off another series of changes. In this way the impulse can move along the fiber with no reduction in size, since it is continually being regenerated. The action potential causes the inside of the fiber to become positive. Current flows from this positive region to the negative region ahead. The membrane potential in the inactive negative region is reduced to the threshold, and an impulse fires off in this section of the fiber also.

SALTATORY CONDUCTION

The chief trouble with this process is that it takes time to change the permeability of the membrane to sodium. Since this change has to take place at every point along the nerve fiber, the transmission of the impulse is relatively slow. We saw that one of the crucial stages was the flow of current inside the fiber from the positive active region to the negative inactive region. This current flows in a minute electric circuit, since it flows to the negative region then out through the membrane and back along the outside of the fiber. It reduces the potential difference between the inside and the outside of the fiber, altering its permeability to sodium. The fast part of the process is the current flow, the slow part is the change in permeability to sodium. If it were possible to increase the part which the current plays, the speed of impulse transmission could be greatly increased. This can be done.

In many nerves there is no sort of insulating sheath around the axon. Current can pass across the axon membrane at all points along the nerve. It does do this, and therefore at all points there is a time-consuming change in sodium permeability. If we were to measure the speed of conduction in this type of fiber we should find it to be rather slow. In many nerve fibers, however, conduction is much faster. In these faster fibers, surrounding each axon there is an insulating layer of a type of fat known as myelin. This insulating layer does not cover the whole fiber. It is interrupted at regular intervals and the axon surface is exposed. These interruptions were first properly described by a histologist, Ranvier, and in his honor they have become known as nodes of Ranvier. If the myelin really does insulate the axon surface, it is clear that current will only be able to cross the membrane at the uninsulated nodes. If this is so, no change in membrane potential will take place along the internodes; the membrane potential will never be reduced to the threshold value, and there will be no change in sodium permeability. This means that the impulse will travel at the speed of ordinary electric current along the internodes. The active process at the nodes is of course, essential to continually regenerate the action potential which would otherwise gradually fade away. By confining it to the nodes, however, and allowing

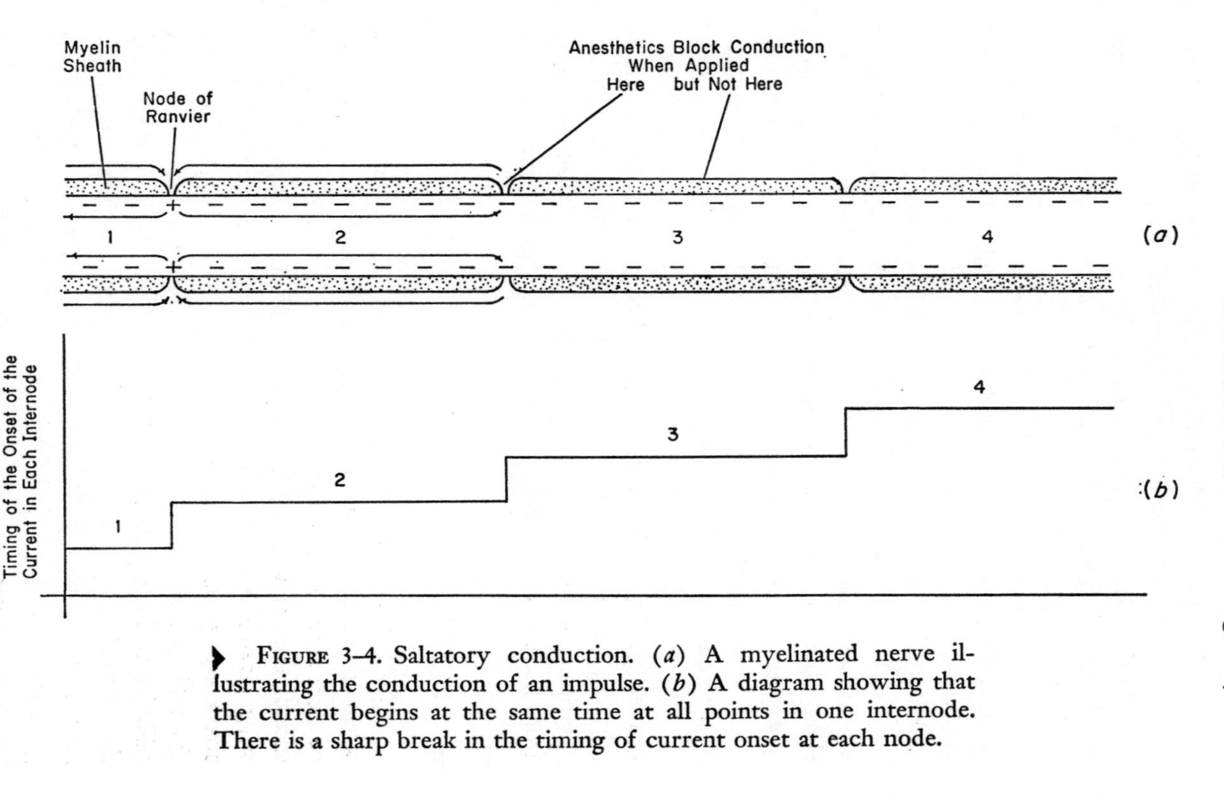

▶ FIGURE 3–4. Saltatory conduction. (*a*) A myelinated nerve illustrating the conduction of an impulse. (*b*) A diagram showing that the current begins at the same time at all points in one internode. There is a sharp break in the timing of current onset at each node.

conduction to proceed by ordinary electrical means in the internodes, the speed of conduction is made much greater.

If this idea is correct, we can make some predictions which can be tested. Some of these are very complex but we can easily understand two of them.

(1) Anesthetics and other substances which do not interfere with ordinary electric conduction, but which block biological processes, should have no action when applied to the internodes. When applied to the nodes they should block conduction.

(2) If the internode is acting simply as a conductor, when an impulse passes, the current at all points along an internode should begin and end at the same time. This, of course, happens in any simple electric circuit. Because of the delay at each node there should be a clear break between the timing of the current flow in one internode and that in the next.

Both predictions have been found to be correct, and there can be no doubt that the process takes place. It is known as saltatory conduction, from the Latin *salto*—I leap. It is a very apt description since the impulse does leap at the speed of electricity from node to node, being renewed in strength at each one.

REFRACTORINESS

So far we have been discussing what processes take place when one stimulus is applied to a nerve. What happens when two or more are applied, one after the other? Suppose that we give two stimuli, each of which is just large enough to produce an impulse when given alone. If a long time interval separates the two stimuli, two action potentials are produced. If the time interval between the two is made shorter, a point is reached when the second stimulus will not generate an impulse. If we still keep the stimuli the same time apart but gradually increase the intensity of the second one we shall find that eventually a second impulse is again generated: the threshold is higher than before. If the time interval between the two is further shortened, eventually the second

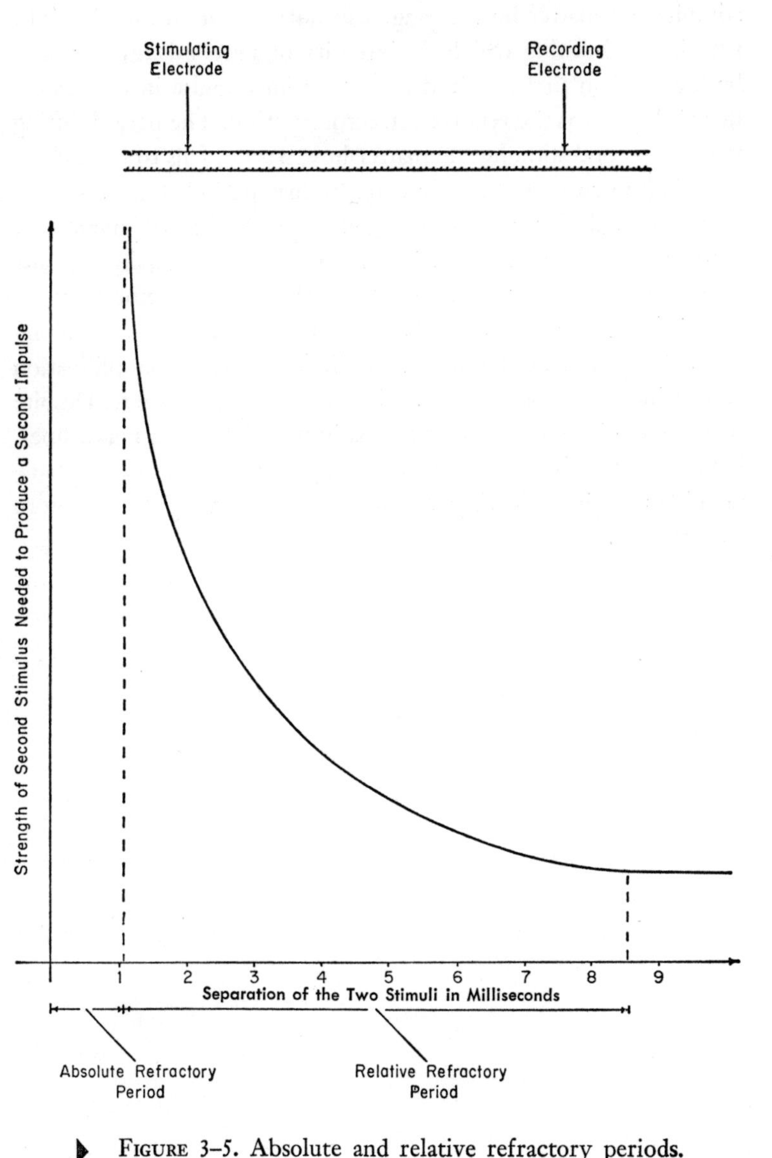

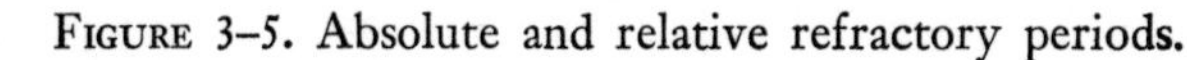

▶ FIGURE 3–5. Absolute and relative refractory periods.

stimulus, no matter how strong, will not fire off an impulse. The time interval during which the intensity of a second stimulus must be higher than that required to fire off an impulse in the resting fiber is known as the relative refractory period. The period during which a second stimulus, no matter how strong, fails to fire off the fiber is known as the absolute refractory period. Refractoriness is due to the difficulty of initiating an impulse while the membrane is still permeable to sodium. When the membrane again becomes impermeable to sodium an impulse can be produced normally.

This short account of the way in which impulses pass along nerve fibers has been much simplified. Insofar as simplification always introduces some error, it is also slightly inaccurate. Despite this it does give an outline of the basic properties of a nerve fiber. If you can clearly understand these explanations, you should have no difficulty in following the detailed accounts given in more advanced books.

4 Chemical Controls

In English we have a very rich variety of words which we can use for ridicule or abuse. Cretin is one of these. It conjures up a picture of someone completely incompetent in every way—dull, unimaginative, and without energy. Yet when we use this word, do we really understand what it means? In Switzerland, a high, mountainous country, far from the sea, a large number of abnormal children used to be born. Physically they grew up to be grossly deformed. They were small and fat with very rough skin and coarse features. Mentally they were completely retarded and grew up as imbeciles. These children were called cretins. Only in the second half of the last century did doctors realize that in all these cases the thyroid gland in the front of the neck was small and nonfunctional. Someone daringly suggested that the injection of extracts of animal thyroid glands might help these children to live normal lives. When treatment began early enough the result was dramatic: the children so injected rapidly improved and grew up to be relatively normal people. This was one of the first great modern triumphs of medicine. Clearly the thyroid normally produces some substance which has widespread effects. The brain, the skin, the muscles, the bones, indeed all the cells in the body, fail to develop properly in its absence. In cretins the gland fails to produce the substance and the result is disastrous. Yet by injecting thyroid extract, even from another animal, the deficiency can be removed, and development can become normal. This treatment formed part of the foundation for an advance into one of the most exciting fields in modern medicine and physiology, that of endocrinology.

If we were to look at the structure of the thyroid, we would find that it has no ducts from which the substances it produces can be discharged. These substances seem to be simply released into the blood which flows through the gland and then to pass into the general body circulation. In this way they are carried to every region of the animal. The salivary glands, on the other hand, discharge their secretions into a duct which carries them into the mouth. There is no question of discharging the saliva into the blood stream; it has a special job to do in preparing the food for swallowing, and the duct ensures that it reaches the right place. Glands which discharge their secretions into a duct to be released at a specific point are known as exocrine; those which discharge their secretions into the blood are known as ductless, or endocrine. The secretions produced by the endocrine glands are called hormones.

CHEMICAL MEDIATION BETWEEN CELLS

We have already seen that when a nervous impulse reaches a synapse it causes a chemical transmitter to be released. This in turn acts on the surface membrane of the next neuron in the system; an impulse is produced in this second neuron and the transmitter itself is rapidly destroyed. The process is similar when an impulse in a motor nerve reaches a muscle fiber or a salivary gland cell. A chemical is released and the muscle fiber contracts or the gland cell secretes. To prevent the muscle fiber contracting repeatedly or the gland cell continuously secreting after only one impulse, the chemical transmitter is destroyed as soon as it has produced its effect.

The thyroid hormone and the chemical transmitter released by a neuron are so different that it might seem ludicrous for us to try to find common ground between them. Yet that common ground is there. Both these substances play a vital part in the controlled integration of the body's activity; both are released by one cell and produce a change in another cell. They are very different in the extent of spread of these effects. The transmitter normally only alters the activity of one cell, whether it be the next neuron, a single muscle fiber, or a single gland cell. It is strictly localized and immediately destroyed. The thyroid hormone can, and does, change every cell in every part of the body. It is not localized to one tiny region, and there does not appear to be any mechanism for its immediate destruction. Its effects are long-term and widespread. The difference between the two methods of integration can perhaps be made clearer by an analogy. Imagine a small country town, Popeye Gulch, which has been told that in six months' time the president of the country is going to visit it. The mayor naturally wants his home town to make a very good impression on its distinguished visitor. So, six months before the visit, he sends out a circular letter to all the citizens. In it he tells them that the president is coming and urges them to make a special effort over the next six months to ensure that their gardens are as attractive as possible on the day that the great man arrives. The letter has its desired effect. Husbands urge on their wives, wives urge on their husbands, and soon all the gardens are looking more attractive than they have ever done before. Then on the day before the visit the mayor drives round to ensure that everything is spick and span. To his horror he sees that the grass on Mr. Brown's front lawn is long and untidy. As soon as he returns to his office he angrily telephones Mr. Brown and tells him to mow his lawn. Mr. Brown does so and removes the last blot on the face of Popeye Gulch. The circular letter is rather like the thyroid hormone: it goes out to every unit in the community, it alters the activity of each of those units, it produces its effect over a long period. On the other hand, the telephone call is rather like the nervous transmitter: it acts on only one unit, Mr. Brown, and it produces its effect immediately. In general we can say that the nervous system produces rapid, short-term changes limited to the cells on which the activated nerves end. The hormonal system is more concerned with long-term adaptations which may involve all the cells in the body.

However, like all generalizations, this one gives us a useful but slightly inaccurate picture of the situation. The thyroid hormone and the nervous transmitter are at the two extremes of chemical mediation between cells; there are a host of examples which lie in between. The sex hormones have effects which are almost as wide as those of the thyroid hormone. They can alter the texture of the skin, the deposition of fat, and the strength of muscles. But while these general effects are important, they have a much more marked action on certain special regions. The male sex hormone produces changes in the larynx, causing the familiar breaking of the voice as the boy grows up to become a man. The female sex hormones produce the development of the breasts as the girl becomes a woman. In both sexes these hormones are responsible both for the external form and internal structure of the genital organs. There are obviously generalized widespread actions on all cells, but the effects on the structure particularly associated with sex are much more marked.

Several hormones produced by the pituitary gland are even more specific in their action. This tiny piece of tissue, situated in a very inaccessible position inside the skull at the base of the brain, is probably the most important gland in the body. It produces hormones which control the growth and development of most of the other endocrine glands, and it has been called "the foreman of the endocrine factory." The pituitary hormones are still released into the general circulation, but some of them, far from having widespread effects, only alter the activity of one other organ in the body. The thyroid-stimulating hormone, or TSH, as its name suggests, keeps the thyroid gland active but it does not directly influence any other tissue. Similarly, the gonadotropins control the testes in the male and the ovaries in the female, while the adrenocorticotropic hormone, or ACTH, governs the activity of the adrenal cortex.

We can see one further stage in increasing specificity. The pituitary lies immediately below the part of the brain known as the hypothalamus, and the two are linked by a slender stalk. There is a peculiar arrangement of blood vessels between the two called the pituitary portal system. These vessels collect venous blood from the hypothalamus and convey it along the pituitary stalk to the gland cells. The hypothalamic neurons secrete chemicals into this blood system. When these substances reach the pituitary they alter the output of hormone from the gland cells. Work is at the moment going on in an effort to isolate these chemicals. There may be one type of hypothalamic substance for each pituitary hormone but this idea still awaits confirmation.

We can outline five general types of chemicals which are released from one type of cell and control the activity of other types of cell. We must emphasize that these are not rigid divisions. Each group of substances does not have properties which can be sharply distinguished from those of adjacent groups. Rather we can see a gradual gradation of types. At one extreme the nervous transmitter only excites the cells in its immediate vicinity and is rapidly destroyed. The hypothalamic substances govern the activity of a few cells in the pituitary; when released into the general circulation they are too dilute to have any effects. The pituitary hormones concerned in control of the thyroid, adrenals, and gonads are released into the general circulation but only affect a single gland or gland pair. The sex hormones modify most of the cells of the body in some way but are particularly concerned with the reproductive system. Finally the thyroid hormone appears to have a general effect on all the cells of the body.

CONTROL

If the hormone system is to be effective in organizing the activity of the body, it must be controlled in some way. There must be a mechanism which arranges that just the right amount of hormone is released. Either too little or too much would probably produce unwanted results. Consider the thyroid hormone: too little produces an animal which is sluggish and dull, too much a nervous, excitable creature. The output from the gland is controlled by the thyroid-stimulating hormone from the pituitary. In turn the latter is governed by a factor passing down the portal system of vessels from the hypothalamus. This region of the brain seems to be the highest part of the control system. But, you may ask, how does the hypothalamus know how much factor must be released into the portal system? Remarkably, by an unknown mechanism, it estimates the quantity of thyroid hormone in the blood. If there is too little, the output of the hypothalamic factor into the portal system is altered. This increases the output of TSH, which in turn causes a faster release of thyroid hormone, so raising the blood concentration of the latter. If there is too much thyroid hormone in the blood, the reverse process takes place, and the output of TSH is depressed. When the thyroid hormone is at just the right concentration there is no change in the output of the hypothalamic factor. This type of mechanism is known as a negative feedback. It is very similar in principle to the mechanism which operates the ordinary household thermostat. As you know, thermostats are very commonly used to keep a tank of water at a particular temperature. Heat is supplied to the water by means of an electric coil. This raises the water temperature which is measured by a special type of thermometer. This thermometer is so arranged that when it rises above a certain level, the electric circuit is broken, and the supply of heat cut off. The water cools down and when the temperature falls below the set level, the electric current is turned on again. In this way we can keep a water tank at an approximately constant temperature. Our central heating system gets neither too hot nor too cold, but remains just right. The relationship between the thyroid, the adrenals, and the gonads, on one hand, and the pituitary, on the other, is very similar to this. For instance, we can regard the concentration of the thyroid hormone in the blood as the temperature, the output of TSH as the electric current which tends to raise this tempera-

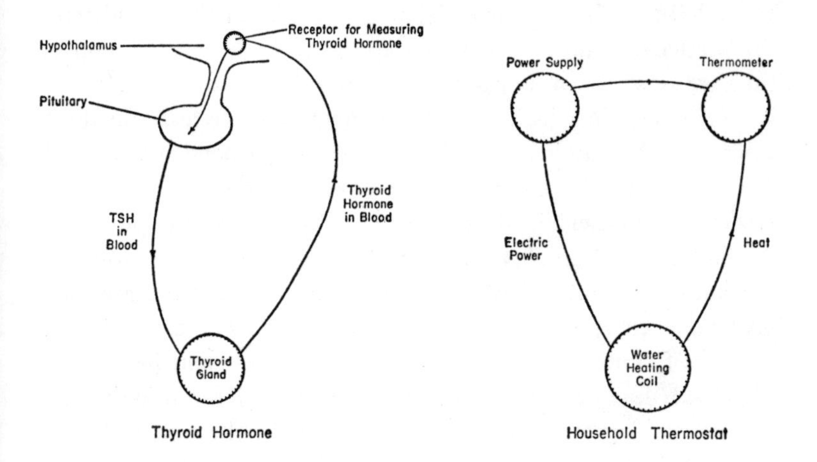

▶ FIGURE 4–1. A comparison of control in the endocrine system and in a household thermostat.

ture, and the hypothalamus as the thermometer which cuts off the supply of current when blood levels of thyroid hormone become too high. The analogy must not be pressed too far, but it is interesting to note that both engineers and the human body have evolved similar sorts of mechanisms to solve their control problems.

Unfortunately, things are not quite so simple as might appear at first sight and there are several unanswered questions. How, for instance, is the appropriate blood level for the hormones set? Once the setting has been made we can easily visualize how variations are prevented. It is not so easy to see how the original setting can be made. In a thermostat the equivalent question is: "What decides the temperature around which the small variations will take place?" Here the setting depends on the way in which the thermometer is arranged. Presumably in the body it depends on some mechanism in the hypothalamus which is the equivalent of the thermometer in the thermostat. What this mechanism is and how it operates are completely unanswered questions.

Another major problem is the balance between the synthesis

and release of the hormones from the glands. In the gonads and the adrenals the hormones do not appear to be stored. As soon as they are synthesized they are set free into the blood stream. There is no reservoir in which they can be held before release. In these cases the only way in which the level of the hormone in the blood can be altered is by controlling the rate of synthesis in the gland. However, in other glands, notably the thyroid and the pituitary, we find a more complex situation. These glands are able to store the hormone which they produce. Clearly, here there are two possible levels at which control could operate. There could be a control of synthesis of the hormone, and there could be control of release. Imagine two pumps which are used for bringing up subterranean water to irrigate a dry farm. In the first case, the water comes straight out of the outlet pipe of the pump into the irrigation channel. In the second, it goes first of all into a large tank. In the first case, the only way in which we can alter the supply of water to the irrigation channel is by altering the rate of pumping. This is analogous to the gonads and adrenal cortex where the only way the supply of hormones to the blood can be altered is by altering their rate of synthesis. With the second type of pump there are two levels at which we can control the situation. As in the first case we could alter the rate of working of the pump, but in addition, by means of a tap, we can also control the outflow from the tank. The tank outflow would be a fine control since it would be impossible for very long periods to produce an outflow that was markedly different from the pumping rate. Suppose we half closed the tap, making the outflow from the tank much less than the inflow. The tank would fill up and then overflow, thus making the total outflow from the tank, even though by another route, equal to the inflow. If with a full tank, we opened the tap wide, the outflow would be much greater than the inflow. The tank would soon become empty and once more the outflow would be equal to the inflow. Thus the general level of flow is set by the rate of pumping. Small variations can be made in the hour-by-hour operation of the system by varying the outflow from the tank. The control of pumping rate may be called the coarse control, that of the outlet tap, the fine one. The situation is probably very similar in glands like the thyroid and pituitary. The general blood level of the hormone is set by controlling the rate of synthesis. Day to day, and hour to hour, variations around this are brought about by controlling the rate of release. We shall not be able to properly understand how hormones control and integrate bodily activity until we discover the mechanisms which balance the rates of synthesis and release of endocrine products. Unfortunately, we are still a long way from this goal. How far will be seen when we come to consider the individual glands in a later section of this book. Yet a long road has been traveled since the days when cretins were commonplace. The rarity of this condition today is encouraging evidence of our dawning understanding of the endocrine control system.

5 Collecting Information

There is a strange disease in which infants are born without the ability to detect pain. We often imagine pain to be a nuisance. While suffering from an agonizingly painful tooth or a severe headache, who has not wished that pain could be totally abolished? We do not really believe our parents when they tell us that pain is a useful sensation and that we should be grateful for it. We would no longer be unbelieving if we could see one of those children born without the ability to feel pain. Such people are often sadly deformed simply because they are unable to detect dangerous stimuli. A child, whom I know, as an infant thrust his hand into a fire. He felt no pain and before he could be rescued his hand was severely damaged. Such unfortunates are crippled by their inability to gather information about dangerous aspects of their environment.

Other types of sensory disability, such as blindness and deafness, are much more common. The disadvantages of these conditions are clear. Everyone has heard of blind people who keep falling over or of deaf people who are injured in road accidents because they fail to hear approaching vehicles. These few examples show conclusively how important it is to be able to gather information about the external environment; sense organs which collect this type of information are known as exteroceptors. There are also receptors which collect information about the state of the gut. They tell us when the stomach is empty or the rectum is full and are known as enteroceptors. These too are providing information about regions which are usually regarded as outside the body proper. The gut is an open-ended tube running through the animal body. Food materials are not considered to have entered the body until they have been digested and have passed through the gut wall.

The need for these two types of receptor is obvious. They collect information and supply it to the brain, which then directs the muscles and glands to work in an appropriate way. A pinprick on the foot causes the leg to be drawn away from the stimulus. The sight of an appetizing meal causes the central nervous system to issue directions for the secretion of digestive juices in the mouth and stomach. On the whole, we are conscious of the functioning of this type of sensory receptor. Not only does the appearance of food cause the secretion of digestive juices, but we actually see and smell the food and feel satisfied and full when we have eaten it. There is, however, a large and important group of receptors of whose functioning we are not usually aware. These are the proprioceptors. They provide the brain with information about the internal state of the various regions of the body. You may perhaps be unable to see immediately why it should be necessary for an organism to have these proprioceptors. Once again an analogy may help. If we are in Woodchuck City and have to get to Squirrelville for a meeting, there are two things which we must know about Squirrelville. We must know where it is in relation to Woodchuck City, and how far it is from Woodchuck City. The first piece of information tells us in what direction we must travel; the second tells us what time we must leave in order to arrive on time. Suppose now that instead of leaving from Woodchuck City, we are starting out from Marmot Town, which is much further away in the opposite direction. Squirrelville is still in the same place, but in order to reach it we must travel in a different direction and leave at a different time. It is so obviously true as to be almost ridiculous that in order to reach Squirrelville for our meeting, we must know where we are starting out from.

Now consider the problem of a man who is sitting at a desk and wishes to pick up a pen which is lying there. Suppose in one situation his arm is resting on the desk and in another it is hanging by his side. In both situations the pen is in the same position on the desk but the movement which the man must make is quite different in the two cases. Before it can tell the arm where to move, the brain must be informed of the position of the arm. It receives this information from proprioceptors in the muscles and the joints. Whatever activity the body carries out can only be done efficiently if there is an efficient system of telling the brain what the state of the body is at the beginning of that activity. Proprioceptors provide the central nervous system with a host of information, from the state of contraction of a muscle to the temperature of the blood. We are not usually aware of this type of information reaching our brains, but it is absolutely essential if our bodies are to function in a healthy way.

Any receptor must be able to detect information about a particular property of its environment and translate it into a nerve impulse. In order to be useful, a receptor should be able to distinguish between different aspects of its surroundings. Thus there are receptors in the skin which are sensitive to pressure while the receptors in the retina are sensitive to light. With all receptors, however, a great sensitivity to one type of stimulus does not mean that they will be completely unable to pick up other types. This is easily illustrated in the retina where the receptors are particularly highly developed and specialized. Everyone knows that a bang on the head can produce amazing visions of stars and bright lights. These are caused by retinal receptors firing off in response to an extreme form of another type of stimulus. This can be demonstrated in a slightly more refined way by closing an eye and pressing on the side of the eyeball. As pressure increases, patches of color and bright lights will probably be seen. This illustrates a very important principle of sensory reception, namely, that the nature of the sensation depends on the neuron which initiated the impulse. In the nerve fiber leading from a retinal receptor, all nerve impulses, once initiated, are identical and indistinguishable from one another. The system is designed to detect light, and even if an impulse is generated by a severe pressure change, the apparent sensation will be one of light and stars. The type of sensation that results depends on the peripheral neuron and on the connections made in the central nervous system. A single impulse in a neuron is totally indistinguishable from another single impulse; no matter what the nature of the stimulus, the apparent sensation will be the one which that particular system is designed to detect.

Very little is known about what makes a receptor very sensitive to one type of stimulus but almost completely insensitive to others. For instance, in the skin there are usually considered to be four different types of sensation. These are touch (and pressure), pain, heat, and cold. There are particular spots on the skin which are highly sensitive to one type and much less sensitive to others. If a warm pointer touches various points on the skin, some will respond with a feeling of warmth while others will not. These warm spots can be plotted on a chart. Similar patterns can be demonstrated for cold and touch receptors. If the warm, cold, and touch spots are marked with ink, the tiny pieces of marked skin can be cut out. When these are examined by methods currently available, it is impossible to demonstrate any difference in the sensory endings beneath each type of spot. It used to be thought that each type of sensory neuron had an elaborate structure at its end which made it particularly sensitive to one type of stimulus. Modern experiments show that no clear distinction can be demonstrated between the skin endings which detect the different types of stimulus. It is conceivable that with better methods, different types of nerve ending might be found but the problem has so far proved insoluble.

The study of sensation has in many ways been a poor relation in neurophysiology. The chief difficulty is that often, when a sensory route is stimulated, there is no obvious consequence. There is no clearly defined output to a sensory system. When a motor nerve to a muscle is excited, the muscle twitches and this can be easily and precisely observed even in lower animals. However, we obviously cannot ask a frog what it feels when a particular area of skin is stimulated. Thus, it is much easier in lower animals to investigate the motor side of the nervous system than the sensory side. Even in humans, individual differences are so great, and experimental techniques are so limited that comparatively little worthwhile information has been collected.

It is very difficult to do good experiments on conscious sensation. On the other hand, new techniques have provided a great deal of information about the way in which the peripheral sensory neurons respond to stimuli. The most valuable of these methods, in theory simple, in practice very difficult, is the recording in a single nerve fiber of the impulses resulting from a particular type of stimulus. The physiologists who first did this rapidly produced convincing evidence to show that while cutaneous sensory nerves might not be distinct anatomically when examined by the best available methods, they certainly behaved very differently. Each fiber responded at a very low threshold to one particular type of stimulus and only at a much higher threshold to others. It is not particularly easy to see just why a particular fiber should be very sensitive to touch but not to warmth, while another has the reverse properties. It must be admitted that it is extraordinarily difficult to imagine how this could happen unless there is something basically different in the fine structure of the nerve endings. If this is so, it has up to now completely eluded investigators.

Some of the problems of sensory receptor study and some of the tentative answers which have been given are well illustrated by Professor Y. Zotterman's experiments on the temperature sense in the tongue. He recorded from single sensory fibers in the nerves leaving the tongue. The rates of impulse discharge were measured when hot or cold stimuli of varying intensity were applied to the tongue surface. He found that there were two different types of receptor. One had a maximum rate of discharge at a temperature above that of the normal body. The other discharged at its highest rate when the temperature was low. In both cases, moving the temperature in either direction away from the point of maximum sensitivity resulted in a diminished rate of impulse production. This simple experiment provided a great deal of information about the way in which receptors behaved. First of all, it proved that in the case of temperature it was not necessary to have a change of temperature to fire the fiber. Holding the tongue surface at a steady temperature produced a steady rate of impulse discharge. This is not true of all types of sensory information. For instance, it has been found that certain receptors in the joints only fire while a movement is taking place. No impulses are produced when the joint is stationary. Fibers which discharge at a steady rate with a steady stimulus are said not to adapt to that stimulus. Fibers which discharge when a stimulus is applied but whose rate of firing falls off when the stimulus is maintained at a steady level are said to show adaptation.

This idea of adaptation is really a very important one. If you think for a little while you will realize that in order to give a complete picture of many types of stimuli it is necessary to have both slowly and rapidly adapting fibers. Consider the joints, for instance, where there are several types of receptor. There are some whose rate of firing is directly related to the position of the joint. They adapt slowly or not at all and can obviously supply information about the position of that joint even when no movement is taking place. However, it is very often important to be able to collect information about the direction and speed of bending of the joint when a movement occurs. The slowly adapting receptors are quite unsuited to doing this. They cannot send signals which give this type of information to the central nervous system. Other types of fibers are needed. Ideally, there should be one type which does not fire at rest but which is activated when the joint is moved in one direction. There should be another similar group firing when the joint is moved in the opposite direction. The rate of firing of these fibers should then be proportional both to the speed and direction of the movement. Three sets of nerve fibers could therefore give a fairly complete picture of what is happening at a joint. There is, in fact, evidence that all three exist. The slowly adapting fibers give signals as to the actual position of the joint. The rapidly adapting fibers, which respond quickly to change but not to steady stimuli, inform the brain of the direction in which a joint is moving and of the speed of that movement. On the whole, slowly adapting fibers are designed to provide information about steady states while rapidly adapting ones give information about changes.

Returning to the temperature receptors, it is clear that the first stage in reception must be some process which proceeds at one rate at a given temperature and whose rate varies with variations in that temperature. There is a maximum rate of discharge at one particular temperature and both above this and below it the rate falls off. It is interesting to consider the diagram in which the rate of impulse discharge is plotted against the temperature. Corresponding to almost any rate of discharge there are two possible temperatures: one is above that at the peak of the curve, the other is below it. Since the impulses which pass along an axon are identical, it is impossible by looking at a single sensory fiber to decide which of two possible temperatures the fiber is responding to. Only at the peak of the curve is there no ambiguity. The same thing is true of both the hot and the cold fibers when they are considered separately. However, suppose we superimpose the two response curves in the same diagram. There are then no two temperatures at which the pattern of discharge in the two fibers will be identical. When the tongue is hot, the hot fiber alone will be discharging; when it is cold, the cold fiber alone will respond. At intermediate temperatures both fibers will be firing off impulses. If the rate of discharge in each fiber is known, the temperature can be determined without ambiguity. This is a very simple illustration of an important principle. In addition to the rate of discharge of a fiber and the type of stimulus to which it is responding, it is essential to know what is happening in other fibers

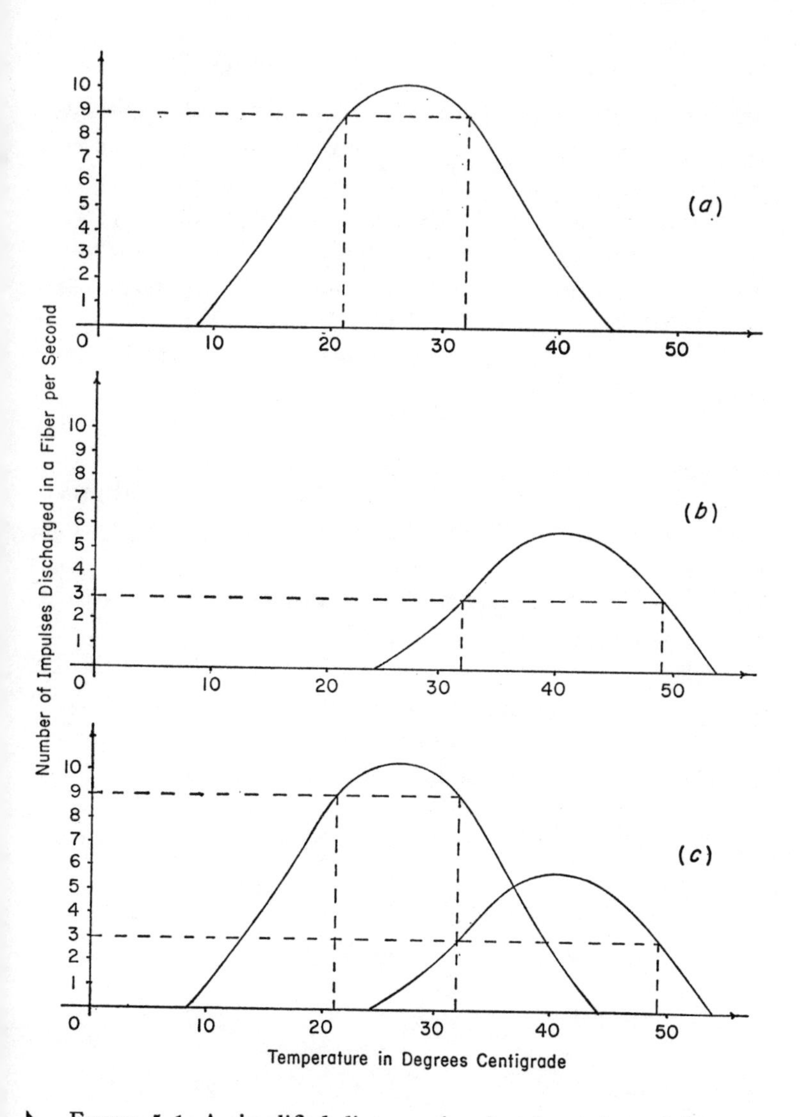

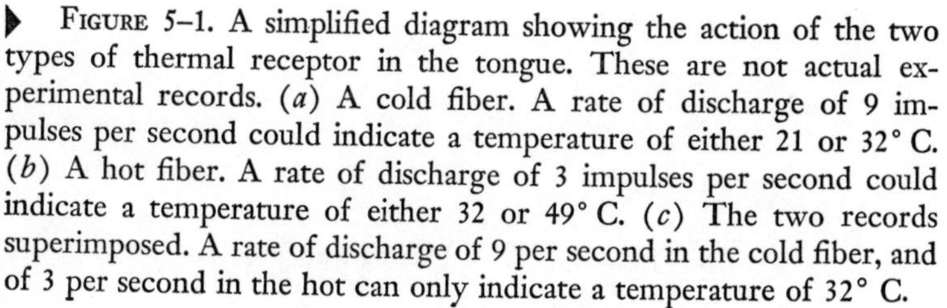

FIGURE 5–1. A simplified diagram showing the action of the two types of thermal receptor in the tongue. These are not actual experimental records. (*a*) A cold fiber. A rate of discharge of 9 impulses per second could indicate a temperature of either 21 or 32° C. (*b*) A hot fiber. A rate of discharge of 3 impulses per second could indicate a temperature of either 32 or 49° C. (*c*) The two records superimposed. A rate of discharge of 9 per second in the cold fiber, and of 3 per second in the hot can only indicate a temperature of 32° C.

before a complete picture of the stimulus can be built up. It seems very unlikely that the rate of discharge in a single fiber can ever provide an unambiguous picture. Ambiguity will only be avoided when the pattern of discharge in a whole series of receptors is taken into consideration. In collecting and sifting information, the central nervous system must take into account discharge patterns in whole groups of fibers as well as discharge rates in individual ones. Only in this way can mistakes of interpretation of the response to a stimulus be avoided.

So far, nothing has been said about the way in which a stimulus actually generates an impulse in a sensory fiber. As with nerve conduction, advances in the understanding of this matter only came about when techniques were developed for recording electrical changes in a single nerve ending. A fairly large nerve ending must be chosen for this sort of investigation and Loewenstein and Rathkamp picked on the Pacinian corpuscle. The corpuscle is usually regarded as being sensitive to mechanical changes such as pressure. It consists of a large nerve ending around which are wrapped a large number of fibrous coverings; it looks, in fact, rather like a miniature onion. In their investigation Loewenstein and Rathkamp first of all peeled off the surrounding layers one by one. Even when all the layers had been removed, the nerve

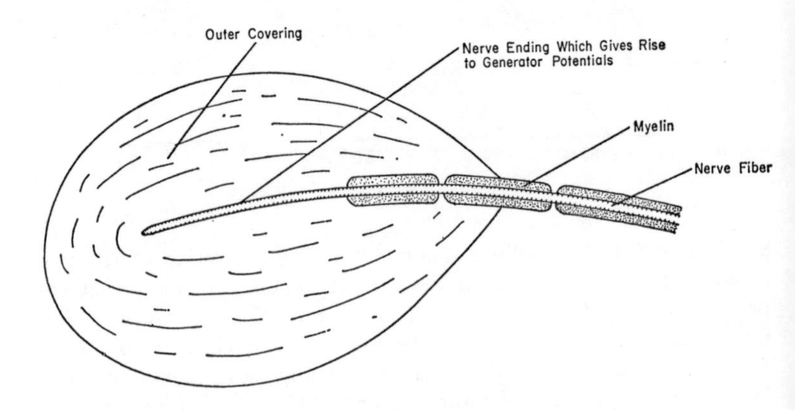

▶ FIGURE 5–2. A Pacinian corpuscle.

ending could still generate an impulse. The outer skins cannot therefore be an essential part of the receptor mechanism, they play no role in firing off a nerve impulse. Photographic studies of an intact Pacinian corpuscle have shown that slow pressure changes are absorbed by the outer layers of skins. The disturbance does not reach the center and fire off a nerve impulse. Only a sharp pressure change is transmitted to the interior of the corpuscle. The elaborate outer part seems to be only a shield which prevents all but fairly sudden stimuli reaching the center and stimulating the actual nerve ending. In order to learn something about the generation of a nerve impulse, we must look at the ending itself.

Once the outer tissue has been stripped off we can see that the central ending is bare and has no myelin sheath. The myelination begins at the edge of the central core of the corpuscle and there is one node of Ranvier between this and the end of the capsule. If a recording electrode is inserted into this nerve ending, very interesting results are obtained. As in a nerve axon, the inside of the nerve ending is electrically negative to the outside. When the ending is stimulated, alternations in this resting potential take place. They are, however, very different in the following ways from the action potentials which can be recorded from an axon.

(1) The potentials are graded in size, a small stimulus producing a small potential change, a large stimulus a large potential change.

(2) When the ending is stimulated, the potential difference between inside and outside tends toward zero. There is no tendency for the inside of the fiber to become positive to the outside.

(3) The potential changes in the nerve ending are not conducted along the membrane of the ending, unlike the nerve impulses which are conducted over the surface of an axon.

(4) There is no refractory period. A second potential can be produced immediately after the first. In fact, the potential

changes produced by two stimuli following immediately one after the other can summate.

(5) The potential changes in the nerve ending are known as generator potentials rather than action potentials.

The generator potentials in the nerve ending are thus of quite a different type from the action potentials in the main part of the fiber. Yet the two are very closely connected. When in a Pacinian corpuscle a mechanical disturbance produces a generator potential the inside of the nerve ending becomes less negative. Current will flow from this less negative region along the nerve ending toward the main fiber; it will tend to reduce the resting potential of the fiber. You may remember that, if the resting potential of a fiber is reduced far enough, changes in sodium permeability take place and an impulse will be generated. If the generator potential is only small, it will only reduce the resting potential of the adjacent part of the fiber a little way. If the generator potential is large enough it will lower the resting potential of the main fiber to the threshold level and fire off an impulse. Thus, as the generator potential increases in size it will cause the resting potential of the main axon to approach threshold, until eventually the disturbance is large enough to produce an impulse. Generator potentials have been shown to occur in all sensory receptors so far investigated. As in the axon, they are produced by a change in the permeability of the membrane of the nerve ending. In this case, however, the change is an increase in permeability to all ions and not just to sodium ions. While this permeability change is in operation, there is a tendency for the concentrations of all ions on the two sides of the membrane to become equal. The barriers to the free diffusion of ions are greatly lowered and the membrane potential tends toward zero. These changes are very similar to those which occur at the neuromuscular junction and will be considered more fully under that heading.

In all sensory receptors a generator potential initiates the nerve impulse, and, so far as is known, this generator potential is always produced by a change in the permeability of the nerve ending to all ions. Since these processes seem to be an essential part of all receptor mechanisms, receptors which are sensitive to different types of stimulus must vary from one another in the way in which the change in membrane permeability is produced. Virtually nothing is known about the ways in which the different stimuli bring about this change. This whole section of sensory physiology is almost a total blank.

It will be appropriate for us to end this chapter with a further discussion of the subject with which it was introduced, pain. Pain seems to result from extreme stimuli of any type. Extreme temperature and extreme pressure are both equally capable of producing pain. It is widely assumed that the very small unmyelinated fibers which are found in all regions in the body are the ones which pick up this familiar and most unpleasant sensation. It is important that the pain fibers should be distributed everywhere so that action can be rapidly taken to deal with unpleasant stimuli in any place. The great physiologist, Sir Charles Sherrington, was the first to point out that pain only results when there is a danger of damage to the tissues. At about 45°C, irreversible damage of the skin is gradually produced and the cells are destroyed. If the skin is gradually exposed to increasing temperature, it is not until 45°C is reached that the sensation of warmth becomes the sensation of pain. It has been suggested that all painful stimuli cause a chemical to be released from damaged cells. This chemical is then supposed to cause the pain fibers to fire. This problem, like so many in sensory physiology, is as yet unsolved. All through this book unanswered questions will be found. We know a great deal about the workings of the nervous system but there is a great deal more yet to be discovered.

6 Our Monitors

No army commander would dream of ordering his troops into battle if he did not know precisely where those troops were. He must have this information so that he can direct the army to attack in the best possible way. Similarly, the pilot of an aircraft which is about to take off must know where on the runway he is, how much luggage he has on board, and how the engines are performing. Otherwise, he would almost certainly crash. Wherever you look in life you find this general principle. In order to give intelligent commands, whether to a machine or to men, the person giving the commands must know just what is happening to the machine or to the men at that particular moment. To take ludicrous examples, it is no good pressing the accelerator if the engine is not switched on, and it is pointless for a manager to summon a workman to his office if that workman is on holiday. An effective command system must be preceded by an effective system for collecting information.

The brain is no exception to this general rule. If it orders a muscle to contract, it must know just what that muscle is doing. It is pointless telling a gland to increase its rate of secretion if the existing rate of secretion is unknown. If our bodies are to be able to move rapidly into action, our central nervous system must be constantly supplied with information about our insides. We are not normally aware of this information reaching our brain; it does not usually reach the level of conscious sensation. The sense organs which collect this information are known as proprioceptors.

Muscle proprioceptors are the ones which have been most studied. They are beautifully adapted for the job they have to do. There are four main types. Branching everywhere are tiny free endings which do not have any special terminal structures; they are thought to be sensitive to pain. The Pacinian corpuscles are probably sensitive to pressure (see Chapter 5). Then there are two types of receptor which respond to tension, and it is with these that we shall be most concerned. They are known as the muscle spindles and the Golgi tendon organs.

The Golgi tendon organs, as their name implies, are found in the muscle tendons. A tendon is made up of a large number of fine fibrils. Each Golgi organ consists of a few of these fibrils enclosed in a capsule. The capsule is pierced by one or two myelinated nerve fibers. Once inside, the neurons lose their myelination and branch widely over the surfaces of the fibrils. If the tendon is put under strain, these little endings are distorted and impulses are fired along the main nerve fibers to which they are connected. The other type of sense organ, the spindle, is found in the main body of the muscle. This time it is a small group of thin muscle fibers which are enclosed in a capsule. We shall call these spindle fibers while the ordinary muscle fibers will be called the large fibers. The spindle fibers are very slender and have contractile tissue at each end: in the middle there is a swollen noncontracting region containing many nuclei. Just like ordinary muscle fibers, the ends of the spindle fibers can contract. We shall call the motor fibers which supply the spindles small motoneurons, to contrast them with the large motoneurons which supply the main muscle. The small motoneurons have a special function which we shall discuss in Chapter 10. As with the Golgi organs, sensory nerve fibers enter the capsule and wrap themselves around the spindle fibers, particularly in the central region.

Each spindle fiber is very richly supplied with these sensory endings.

Is it possible for us to predict the sort of stimuli to which the Golgi organs and muscle spindles will respond? To some extent it is. There are two ways in which the tension in a muscle can be raised. The muscle itself can contract, so tending to become shorter. Alternatively, we can stretch it from outside by pulling on its tendons. In this case, the muscle will clearly tend to become longer. Suppose we were to increase muscle tension in the second way. Both the Golgi organs and the spindles would experience this increase in tension; in both cases the sensory endings would be stretched. If we were recording the activity of the sensory nerve fibers themselves, we should see an increase in their rate of discharge.

On the other hand, contraction of the muscle itself produces a very different situation. As in the first experiment, the tendon will be stretched and the Golgi organs will discharge at a faster rate. Since they are arranged in series with the main muscle fibers, increases in tension in the main fibers are automatically passed on to them. In contrast, the spindles are arranged so that they lie parallel to the main fibers. As the main fibers shorten, tension will be taken off the spindles. The sensory endings in the spindles should therefore be stimulated less and show a decrease in their firing rate.

Although this reasoning seems clear enough, the idea can only be accepted if it is confirmed by experiment. No theory can be proved or rejected until an appropriate technique has been devised for testing it. You might be surprised at how dependent the scientist is on his techniques. We know much more and understand things far more clearly today than we did even ten years ago. This is not because scientists can now think any more clearly than they did in the past, but because the development of new techniques has given them new facts to which they can apply their brain power. Only a very exceptional person can be much ahead of his time in science; the experimenter is so much in the grip of the methods available to him that he finds it extraordinarily difficult to range far into unknown fields. Discovery has two major components: an experimental method which provides reliable facts, and an intelligence able to assess those facts and to suggest new ideas to which they might lead. Either one without the other is useless. The simple technician produces facts which he cannot interpret; the lively mind without facts on which to work can produce nothing but fantasies.

EXPERIMENTS ON MUSCLE RECEPTORS

In the case of muscle receptors, progress was only made when it became possible to study the activity of a single sense organ. Lord Adrian recorded the action potentials in the nerve coming from a minute skin muscle in the frog's chest wall. This tiny muscle contained very few spindles. Even so, when it was stretched, the record of action potentials from the whole nerve was far too complex for a clear analysis to be made. Adrian had somehow to simplify matters. He very carefully stripped off the muscle fibers one by one until just a single muscle spindle was left. The record then became relatively simple. The rate of impulse discharge gradually increased as the muscle was stretched. The greater the stretch, the greater was the strain on the receptors, and the faster they fired impulses. You can no doubt see what the great disadvantage of this technique is. Although it gives clear results, the muscle must be destroyed in the process. It can be applied only in a very limited number of cases.

Sir Bryan Matthews, like Adrian working in Cambridge, England, then devised a method which could be used much more widely. With this new technique, simplified results were obtained with the muscle still intact. This was achieved by recording the activity of a single nerve fiber, rather than of the whole nerve. Matthews divided a small strand from the nerve and teased this out. Eventually he obtained a single axon which responded in a relatively simple way when the muscle was stretched. Since the axons coming from the various sensory receptors in muscle appear identical, it is impossible to decide just by looking at an axon what sort of information it is carrying. Whether the receptor at the end of the fiber is a Golgi organ, a muscle spindle, or some other type must be deduced from the way the activity changes under different experimental conditions.

Using this technique, which has been applied by many workers, the major facts about muscle sensory receptors have been discovered. Two quite different types of receptor have been found to respond to stretch. In one experiment, tension was imposed on the muscle from outside by stretching it. At the same time, the discharge rate in a single sensory axon from that muscle was measured. Then, while the stretch was still kept up, the muscle was made to twitch by giving an electric shock to the main part of its nerve. Once again the tension in the muscle was raised, but this time by contraction of the muscle itself rather than by outside stretch. As usual, the receptor discharge was recorded. Most of the sensory axons fell into one of two groups.

The first type of sense organ, which Matthews called A, fired off impulses when very light stretch was applied to the muscle. As you might expect, the rate of discharge increased as the muscle was stretched more and more. What you might not expect is what happens when a muscle twitch is superimposed on a steady stretch. The A type of receptor, for a moment, completely ceased to fire off any impulses. As soon as the twitch was over, it began to fire again. So here we have a sense organ whose discharge increases in proportion to the tension in the muscle, when that tension results from stretching the muscle. When an increase in tension is brought about by the muscle itself contracting, even the resting discharge of the A type of receptor ceases. Matthews tried to find the position of these receptors in a muscle. He discovered that, when he was recording from an A-type axon, local heat and pressure altered the firing rate only when they were applied to the belly of the muscle. They had no effect when applied to the tendon. We may reasonably come to the same conclusion that Matthews himself came to. The A receptors must be somewhere in the main part of the muscle (see Figure 13–2).

In a B-type unit, there was a very different pattern of activity. Low tensions were quite unable to produce any discharge. Very much greater stretches than those which fired the A receptors had to be imposed before the B receptors fired. Suppose that we were to do such an experiment and to measure the tension required to fire off the B receptors. Suppose then that we set the tension just below this threshold value. We should, of course, see no discharge. What would happen if we stimulated the main nerve and caused the muscle to twitch? If the B receptor behaved like the A, we should still see no response. But it does not. The twitch would, in fact, produce a discharge in our axon. If the steady stretch was already above threshold for the B sense organ, a twitch would only increase its rate of discharge. So, in contrast to the A type, the B receptors have a high threshold, and they respond to increases of tension in the muscle, no matter how that tension is produced. The response to local heat and pressure suggests that the sense organs which behave in this way are probably to be found in the tendon and not in the muscle belly.

So the A receptors have properties which can be explained only if we assume that they are arranged parallel to the main muscle fibers. Stretching the muscle, and thereby lengthening it, increases their rate of discharge. Contraction of the muscle, which shortens it, blocks the discharge. Everything points to the muscle spindle being the organ responsible. Lengthening the muscle would put a strain on a muscle spindle, shortening it would take the strain off again. In complete contrast, with the B receptor it did not matter whether the muscle itself contracted or was stretched. Increase of tension in either of these two ways fired off the sense organ. This time the receptor must be arranged in series with the main muscle fibers. In both cases, the tension in the tendon will increase. The fact that application of local heat and pressure there also altered the B-type discharge points fairly conclusively to the Golgi tendon organ. The speculations which we made earlier in this chapter are confirmed. These results are now universally accepted, and the enormous importance of these proprioceptors in the control of muscle movement is clearly recognized. We shall be learning more about them in chapters 13 and 14.

THE FIRING OF A STRETCH RECEPTOR

Matthews' beautiful experiments were limited in that they recorded only in the axon the impulses produced by the stretch receptor. At that time, it was quite impossible to investigate in any detail the way in which impulses actually began. The experiments on generator potentials in the Pacinian corpuscle had not been performed; nothing was known about the origin of an impulse at a sense organ. Only in recent years have physiologists even known what to look for. Professor Stephen Kuffler decided to work on the particularly interesting stretch receptors which are found in lobster muscles. In a mammal, the sensory neurons have their cell bodies in the sensory nerve trunk just before it enters the spinal cord. In the lobster the arrangement is somewhat different. There are no muscle spindles and the sensory neurons have their cell bodies right next to the muscle fibers. Processes, called dendrites, pass out from a cell body and spread over the surface of a muscle fiber. When the muscle is stretched, or itself contracts, these dendrites are put under strain, and, if the stimulus is great enough, an impulse is produced in the neuron. By careful manipulation, a microelectrode could be pushed into the sensory cell and a record made of all the changes which followed stretch of the muscle. The inside of the resting cell was 70 to 80 mV negative to the outside. Just as in an ordinary neuron, when an impulse was fired off, the inside became positive to the outside.

Kuffler was interested in trying to detect any electrical changes which might occur in the dendrites. He wanted to know if they took place before an impulse was actually fired in the main part of the cell. He was on the right track; very tiny potential changes could be picked up on stretching the muscle. If an extremely tiny stretch was imposed these potentials could be detected, even though no impulse was fired off. Unlike an impulse, these potentials were graded in size in proportion to the intensity of the stretch. They differed from all-or-nothing impulses in another way too. They persisted and could be picked up for as long as the muscle was being stretched. In fact, they were very similar to the Pacinian corpuscle generator potentials. The strain on the dendrites when the muscle is stretched probably increases the permeability of their surface membranes to all ions. This tends to make the inside of the dendrites less negative. The electrical change is conducted along the dendrites to the main cell. There the resting membrane potential is also reduced. If a number of dendrites act together like this, the cell resting potential is lowered to its threshold value. An impulse is fired off.

In the lobster stretch receptor there are two types of membrane. This seems to be true for many kinds of excitable tissues. In one membrane graded responses can be produced. These vary in size according to the intensity of the stimulus. They are not conducted over the surface of the membrane. There is no refractory period and two potentials following closely one after the other can add together. These graded potentials can give rise to electrical changes in the other sort of membrane. The potential difference between inside and outside is reduced. If the change in membrane potential is less than a certain value, the second type of membrane remains inactive. If the change is above this critical value an impulse is produced and is conducted over the membrane surface. Under constant conditions, the impulse remains constant in size. Larger generator potentials do not produce larger impulses. Once an impulse has spread over the membrane, for a moment a second impulse cannot be conducted; the membrane has a refractory period.

In many ways, the firing of an impulse at a sense organ is analogous to the firing of a bullet from a gun. Even if you have fired only a toy gun, you know that the trigger must be pulled back some way before the gun is fired. You can move the trigger a fraction, or you can pull it back almost to the critical point; in either case, so long as you do not actually reach the critical point, the gun will not fire. On the other hand, you can either pull the trigger back to the trigger point extremely gently, or you can suddenly jerk it back; either way a bullet will be fired and will leave the gun at exactly the same speed. You can have a whole series of graded pulls on the trigger, but nothing will happen if you do not reach the critical point. If you do reach the critical point, it will not matter whether you have jerked the trigger or squeezed it gently; a bullet will still be fired and the speed of the bullet will not depend on the way the trigger was pulled.

Receptors can sometimes become adapted to a stimulus, as we saw in Chapter 5. The lobster stretch receptors illustrate this very well. There are, in fact, two types, "fast" and "slow." Up to now we have been thinking about the slow ones. Suppose that we stretch a muscle and hold that stretch at a constant level. The discharge of the slow receptor will not change even if a constant stretch is held for a long period. The slow cell shows no adaptation. The fast receptor is quite different. When the muscle is stretched there will be an initial burst of impulses. Then, even if the stretch is maintained, the rate of firing will fall, and it may even reach the resting level. The fast receptor becomes accustomed to detecting the stretch as it were, and ceases to send information about it back to the central nervous system. It becomes adapted to the stimulus.

Receptors in muscles form only a small part of the whole proprioceptive system. There are chemical receptors which monitor the composition of the blood, receptors which measure the blood pressure, receptors which measure the fullness of the gut, receptors for monitoring every aspect of the body's functioning. For technical reasons, few of these others have been well investigated. Despite this, while they may differ in detail, it is most unlikely that the broad outline of their function will be very different from that which has been found for the sense organs in muscle.

7 The Brain as a Sense Organ

You may be surprised to learn that the brain is one of the most important sensory organs in the body. Not only does it collect information from other regions, not only does it act as the great coordinator, it also acts as a sensory receptor in its own right. Yet the brain is completely enclosed by a bony cavity. No muscles act on it, the pressure changes within the cavity are negligible. It obviously cannot directly collect information about the outside world, and inside conditions appear to be more-or-less constant. But there is no point in continually monitoring something which does not vary. It only makes sense to collect information about something which can change. You may well ask what variable can the brain collect information about. The answer is the blood.

The temperature of the blood is continually changing. If we play football, or run, or take any sort of exercise, our muscles have to work. This work generates heat and the blood becomes warmer. If the temperature of the body is to remain steady, steps must be taken to get rid of this excess heat. Before this can occur, the temperature of the blood must be measured so that the right amount of heat can be eliminated. The brain performs this measurement. When we exercise, another change also takes place in the blood. The muscles use up more oxygen in order to burn

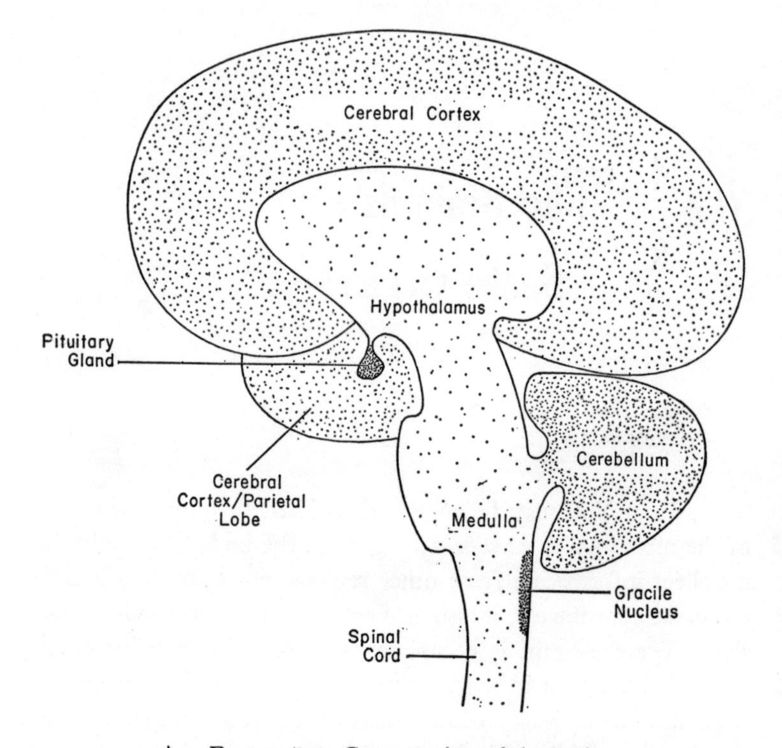

▶ FIGURE 7–1. Cross section of the brain.

the fuel which they use. In turn, more of the end product, carbon dioxide, is produced and passed out into the blood stream. If the muscles are to function properly, the carbon dioxide must be removed from the body and more oxygen must be supplied. The lung movements must become faster and more air must be passed through them. This enables more oxygen to be put into the blood, and washes carbon dioxide out of it. Under normal conditions, the rate of breathing is mainly dependent on the level of carbon dioxide in the blood. If carbon dioxide is added to the air being breathed by a resting animal, that animal breathes more rapidly, even though no exercise is taking place. Somewhere in the body there must be sensory receptors which are sensitive to carbon dioxide. Although there are subsidiary ones associated with the carotid artery, by far the most important receptors are in the brain.

If a college boy goes out on a beer-drinking party, with his beer he takes in large quantities of water. This water is absorbed from the gut and increases the volume of the blood. If our friend were to take in a large amount of water, and afterward did not pass it out, his body would become waterlogged. Everyone knows that this does not occur. The excess water is rapidly eliminated from the body, often to the embarrassment of the individual concerned. If the kidneys know when to pass out excess water there must be sense organs designed to detect this excess. Once again they are in the brain. This time the brain acts on the information in a way which differs from that in the previous two cases. It causes a hormone to be released which passes by way of the blood stream to the kidneys. This is just one example of the close co-ordination between the nervous and endocrine systems.

It is all very well for us to suggest that the brain is working as a sensory receptor, but how can we investigate the precise way in which this occurs? It is certainly a formidable task. It is very difficult to open up the skull and to experiment on the brain without damaging it to such an extent that we can no longer consider it to be working normally. To start with, the investigations must be carried out by rather indirect methods. Only when we have gathered a considerable amount of information in this way, is it possible for us to proceed more directly.

URINE EXCRETION

Professor Verney's experiments on the detection of excess water in the body provide an excellent illustration of the way in which indirect procedures can be used to collect a great deal of information. Verney became very interested in the diuresis which follows the drinking of large quantities of water. This is something which is familiar to all of us. He suspected that the receptors were situated somewhere in the head and that they detected changes in the osmotic pressure of the blood. The dog was used as an experimental animal, and in order to make things easier, a preliminary operation was first performed. Verney anesthetized the dog, opened up the neck and exposed the internal carotid artery which supplies blood to the brain. He pulled the artery outward and sewed up the skin behind it. The artery was protected by enclosing it in a living sheath made from the animal's own skin. The artery was thus exposed right on the surface. After a little training, injections could be made into it without causing any other disturbance to the dog.

In making this preparation, Verney used the classical scientific approach of cutting down the possible variable conditions to a minimum. This precaution is particularly important in experiments on the nervous system, which is expressly designed to detect variations in its environment and act on them. If the normal working of the nervous system is to be investigated, the animal's surroundings must be disturbed as little as possible. The behavior of an anesthetized animal, exposed to the stress of surgery, will clearly differ from that of a normal, intact, and healthy animal. It may be so different as to render the experiment worthless as an investigation of normal physiology. Anesthetics, of course, are used for the specific purpose of blocking the working of part of the sensory system. Great care must be taken to ensure that the particular anesthetic used is not interfering drastically with the function of that part which is under investigation. If possible, experiments must be devised which do not need anesthesia. This does not mean that pain must be inflicted on the animal, since the nervous responses of a creature in agony are possibly even more abnormal than those observed under anesthesia. Verney's work is a beautiful example of how, by performing a preliminary operation, the animal can be kept as free and as normal as possible during the actual experiments. The dogs had become accustomed to having injections into the exposed loop of the carotid artery. The only observed changes in their behavior were due to the substances injected and were not caused by a complex experimental technique.

If we were carrying out an ideal physiological experiment, we should first of all have to obtain an animal in a steady resting condition. We should then give some stimulus to that animal. Lastly, we should look for any changes in the original steady condition which might have been brought about by the stimulus. Each one of these stages is very important and it will be worth our while to consider them in greater detail. Suppose we were doing an experiment to investigate changes produced in a dog's heart rate by injecting a drug. At the beginning, we should have to make sure that the heart was beating steadily and quietly. Only then could we see clearly any changes, particularly if they happened to be small ones. If the heart were jumping around all over the place to start with, we should never be able to get any constant results.

Another thing which bedevils experimenters is the problem of limiting the stimulus to one factor. In our heart-rate experiment, it would be pointless to give the drug by means of a painful injection. The pain itself, even without the drug, would almost certainly make the heart beat faster. We should never know how much of the increase was due to the drug and how much to the pain. A great deal of work is ruined for this very reason. The stimulus contains several components, not one, and it is almost impossible to decide which one of these produced the response.

Physiologists often do bad experiments for another reason. They forget that in order to make deductions about physiology, they must, if possible, use physiological stimuli. Suppose we were studying the action on the heart of adrenaline, which occurs naturally in the body. It would be no good giving a dose of adrenaline a thousand times larger than the amount which is normally found in the blood stream. It would be rather like trying to investigate the working of a small toy electric motor by plugging it in to a high tension supply. We should soon see smoke rising from the coils of the motor and before long it would be completely burned out. This clearly does not mean that it behaves normally in this way. Its normal working could only be studied by wiring it up to the sort of small battery for which it was designed. Similarly, all sorts of strange results might be produced by a drug dosage a thousand times greater than the amount normally found in the body. This does not mean that the drug in the healthy intact animal has these effects.

Neurophysiologists are by no means free from the charge of using unphysiological stimuli. Many experiments involve electrically stimulating various parts of the nervous system. Some useful work has been done by giving electric shocks to a whole nerve or to a part of the brain. But we should never delude ourselves into thinking that we have really discovered something about the physiology of the normal animal until we give stimuli similar to the ones which the body might be expected to meet every day. For instance, we can discover a certain amount about sensation by looking at the response to an electric shock given to a nerve coming from the skin. Ultimately, however, we must look at the responses to touch, to heat, or to some other natural stimulation.

In looking for a response, we must remember the points we made about the first stage of giving the stimulus. If a normal small stimulus is given, the response is likely to be small and we should never be able to see it if the animal were not in a steady, resting condition to begin with. Finally, we must have a means of measuring and permanently recording the changes quickly, clearly and unambiguously. These methods differ from experiment to experiment, but on the whole, the days of stethoscope and stop watch are over. Electronic aids are now standard equipment in all laboratories of physiology.

Verney's experiments clearly illustrate most of these principles. His dogs had been loaded with water and were excreting large amounts of dilute urine. The volume and contents of this urine were measured for a period before the experiment. Various substances were then injected into the carotid loop and their effect on the urine output noted. In all physiological work, control experiments must be performed in which the animal is manipulated in exactly the same way as in the real experiments, but the last stage is omitted. In this case, one possible control would be to prepare the animal in the usual way and to insert the needle, but then not to inject anything. This would check whether the operative procedure itself alerted the urine output.

As mentioned earlier, Verney suspected that there were receptors in the brain sensitive to the osmotic pressure of the blood. He thought that when the blood was dilute and the osmotic pressure low, the kidneys excreted large quantities of dilute urine. When the osmotic pressure was high, on the other hand, he believed that water was retained in the body, and the urine was concentrated and small in volume. Verney therefore began by injecting sodium chloride solutions which were hypertonic. This means that they had an osmotic pressure which was greater than that of the blood. Soon after the injection, the urine flow decreased; the decrease was proportional to the strength of the solution injected. Strong solutions produced a greater inhibition of the urine flow than did the weak ones.

Strong sodium chloride solutions clearly had an effect when injected into the carotid. When injected into other regions of the body the effect, if it occurred at all, was much smaller. There were two possibilities.

(1) The sodium chloride solution produced its effects simply because of its hypertonicity.

(2) The sodium chloride itself produced the response. In this case, other hypertonic solutions would have no effect.

The obvious test was to inject a series of solutions of different compounds. This Verney did, with clear-cut results. Concentrated solutions of quite unrelated compounds slowed down the flow of urine. Their only common property was their hypertonicity. Thus it seems certain that in the brain there are receptors which continually measure the osmotic pressure of the blood. Further work showed that these receptors are probably in the hypothalamus, the region of the brain just above the pituitary gland.

The methods which can be used to localize the position of a brain receptor are illustrated by the work of Andersson and McCann. They were working on a closely related problem, the mechanism which causes an animal to feel thirsty and drink. As with urine excretion, it was suspected that there might be areas in the hypothalamus which were sensitive to osmotic pressure changes. When an animal loses a lot of water, the osmotic pressure of its blood tends to rise. It was thought that this might be the stimulus which produced thirst. A technique was used which has now become very common in neurophysiology. Long, fine needles can be passed through the brain, apparently without causing any disturbance to the animal's behavior. If such a needle were insulated except for the very tip, an electric current could be passed along it and a small area of the brain around the tip stimulated. On the other hand, if the needle were hollow, minute quantities of various solutions could be passed down it. Their effect on a very localized region of the brain could then be investigated.

Andersson and McCann inserted needles into the hypothalamus of a goat and used both techniques. In most parts of the hypothalamus neither electrical stimulation nor injection of strong solutions had any effects on the drinking habits of the goats. In complete contrast, in a few areas, both stimulation and injection of strong solutions caused the goats to drink fantastic quantities of water. Solutions which had the same osmotic pressure as the blood had no effect. This suggests strongly that the goats drank when the needle tip was close to an osmotic receptor. Away from this receptor, neither strong solutions nor electrical stimulation produced a response. The experiments do not actually prove this, however. It is possible that the receptors were in quite another place, but were sending their impulses to the hypothalamus by means of long axons. If this were the case, the stimulation could have been exciting these axons rather than the actual receptors.

On the other hand, axons do not normally fire when solutions like those used by Andersson and McCann are put on their surface. The way in which the goats responded to these solutions makes it very likely that at least some of the receptors responsible for the sensation of thirst are to be found in the hypothalamus.

TEMPERATURE CONTROL

Turning now to quite another field, it is well known that the body temperature of man, and indeed of most mammals, remains steady. Our bodies are at a temperature of about 98.4°F (37°C) and we usually regard variations from this as a sign of disease. Reptiles, amphibians, and other creatures lower than mammals and birds have no means of regulating their temperatures. As a result, the body temperature of, for example, a frog changes with the weather. On a cold day it will be cold and on a warm day it will be warm. In order to maintain a steady temperature, a mammal must have three distinct mechanisms:

(1) For measuring the temperature.

(2) For collecting the information from different receptors and issuing appropriate directions.

(3) For causing heat to be produced or lost, so altering the temperature as required. Here, we are only interested in the first of these, the way in which temperature is measured.

Where in the body do you think would be the best position for these receptors which control the basic body temperature? It would be pointless to have them on the surface of the body which, even in mammals, shows great variations in temperature in different surroundings. There are temperature receptors there, of course, but they are primarily concerned with conscious sensation. They seem to be more important for telling the whole animal how to behave in particular surroundings, than for setting in motion the delicate heat loss and gain mechanisms within the body. On a hot day it is your skin receptors which tell you to move out of the sun into the shade. In the middle of winter, the same receptors tell you either to go indoors or to put on thick woolen clothes. The receptors which actually tell your body to begin sweating in the heat or shivering in the cold are probably situated somewhere else. Receptors in the muscles would be silly since there, as in the skin, the local temperature varies enormously, depending on whether or not the muscle is working. What is needed is a region which reflects the general temperature of the whole body, and which does not vary markedly with local conditions. You can probably see that the blood in some deep part of the body is the best place to take the temperature. Since the blood supplies all regions and is thoroughly mixed up in the heart and great vessels, it accurately reflects the heat content of the body as a whole. Various observations suggested that the temperature of the blood in the head might be important. If the blood going to the head in the carotid artery was warmed by passing it over some heating arrangement, the animal showed all the signs of being too hot. Sweat was secreted and by evaporating cooled the body surface. Blood vessels in the skin opened wide, enabling the blood to carry more heat to the surface. Local heating of parts of the brain by warm water produced similar effects.

Professor Magoun was one of the first people to try to discover precisely where the receptors were to be found. He pushed electrodes into various parts of the dog's brain and produced local heating by passing electric current through them. When this was done in certain areas of the hypothalamus, the dog began to pant and sweat appeared on its footpads (dogs have few sweat glands on the general body surface). These experiments were clearly rather crude; it was difficult to know just how localized was the heating, and whether, in fact, it was the heat and not the electric current which produced the response. A group of Scandinavian physiologists followed up this work, using rather more delicate methods. They stimulated the brain in two ways. With small electrical stimuli, they also found sweating and panting. They showed, in addition, that a similar response occurred when they passed warm water through hollow electrodes. This confirmed the earlier claim that the receptors really were temperature receptors and were not simply responding to electrical stimulation. In order to indicate a response, the Scandinavians used the dilatation of the blood vessels in the skin. This is probably a more sensitive indicator than sweating. They showed that alterations in temperature of only a fraction of a degree could produce a definite dilatation. If the stimulus was kept up for long periods, the response did not become smaller. The receptors did not show any adaptation. Provided that the temperature was changed by the same amount, the response was always the same, no matter whether the change was brought about quickly or slowly. When the temperature remained steady, the degree of dilatation did not change. This confirms that it is the temperature level itself, and not the alteration in temperature, which causes the receptors to fire off. This is important, because it means that the receptors will not give up supplying information, even if the rise or fall in temperature persists for a long time.

Stimulation experiments, like those we have been discussing, can give us a large amount of useful information. Inevitably, they also disturb to some extent the region which is being investigated. Abnormal responses may be seen, although we can greatly reduce the risk of these by keeping the stimulus intensity low. Ultimately, however, all confirmation of ideas in neurophysiology must come from recording the natural activity of the brain. Even then, it is impossible to avoid some disturbance, but it is kept to the very minimum. Unnatural nerve impulses are not introduced. The picture given by the records of the experiment is likely to be very close to what happens under completely normal conditions. In the case of the temperature-regulating mechanism, a little work has been done along these lines. Von Euler placed recording electrodes in the parts of the hypothalamus where earlier work had suggested that the receptors might be found. He then altered the temperature of the blood and looked for any variations in the recorded electrical activity. Slow changes of potential were seen and were found to be closely synchronous with the artificial changes in blood temperature. A rise or fall of as little as one tenth of a degree centigrade could be detected. In contrast, in other areas no potentials which were synchronous with the heat changes in the blood could be recorded. It seems certain that Von Euler was recording the activity of a region closely connected with the regulation of temperature. Once again we must stress that this does not conclusively prove that the actual receptors are in that area. It is possible that the information could be collected elsewhere and then carried by nerve fibers to the hypothalamus. Despite this, it does seem that when we look at all the experiments, we cannot escape the conclusion that some of the thermal receptors are in this part of the brain.

RESPIRATION

We noted earlier that changes in the rate of breathing can be produced by alterations in the amount of carbon dioxide in the blood. We can first find an indication that the receptors for carbon dioxide are in the head in the work of Leon Frederiq at the turn of the century. He very cleverly linked two dogs together in a complicated operation. We shall call these two dogs A and B. The blood from the body of dog A supplied the head of dog B and vice versa. Dog A was forced to breathe more rapidly by artificial respiration. Apart from this, it remained at rest and so only produced the normal amount of carbon dioxide. The artificial faster breathing got rid of this more quickly. Therefore, in the blood supplying the body of dog A and the head of dog B, the carbon dioxide level fell below normal. The breathing of dog B slowed down and sometimes stopped completely. In a second type of experiment, dog A was artificially prevented from breathing. Carbon dioxide was still being produced but could not escape from the lungs. Accordingly, the blood level of carbon dioxide in the body of dog A and the head of dog B rose. Dog B began to respire more rapidly. In both these experiments, as far as dog B was concerned, the principal change was in the carbon dioxide content of the blood supplying the head. Obviously, some carbon dioxide receptors must be in that region.

Gradually the precise position of the receptors was worked out. Various parts of the brain were cut out in animals, but so long as the region just above the spinal cord, known as the medulla, remained intact, breathing was normal. Damage to the medulla often stopped the breathing. It seems likely that some of the carbon dioxide receptors are there. Further work followed the pattern already described for temperature receptors. Solutions containing various concentrations of carbon dioxide were put on the surface of the medulla and injected into it. Several pairs of nerves enter the medulla. Minute amounts of the solutions were put on the medulla just where these nerves entered into it. The rate of breathing was altered more by putting the carbon dioxide solutions on the roots of the ninth and tenth cranial nerves than by injecting them into any other region. Tiny amounts of procaine (a local anesthetic) placed on the roots completely blocked the response. At least some of the receptors for carbon dioxide must be at the roots of these nerves.

You may have been surprised at how important the brain is for collecting information about the state of the blood. In this chapter, we have only come across a few of the sensory receptors which are found there. Some of the others measure the levels of hormones in the blood. We shall be thinking more about them in the chapters on the pituitary gland.

8 The Ear

You may perhaps have never seen someone who is both deaf and blind. Such unfortunate people very rarely venture outdoors. Their disablement is so severe that if they went outside alone, they would almost certainly meet with an accident. They are in this sad state because they have lost the organs of sense which would enable them to collect information from a distance. They can only learn about the world around them by touching objects or bumping into them. They cannot communicate with other people in any of the ordinary ways. Having a friendly chat with their friends or reading an ordinary library book are both out of the question.

In humans, almost all communication between people ultimately depends on either the eye or the ear. All our modern electronic aids for passing information around the world would be useless without sight or hearing to form the first and last links in the chain. Those of you who have elderly relatives may know how difficult it is for even partially deaf people to use the telephone, while for a blind person television loses all its point. We do have a vestige of a third sense, that of smell, which could possibly be used for communicating between individuals. The lower animals can certainly use it in this way. You have only to watch a dog walking along a street to see how much of his world is made up of smells. When meeting another dog, the question as to whether to make love or war is almost always decided by his nose. But we human beings, in the course of evolution, seem to have lost some of our ability to smell things clearly and keenly. We have not lost it entirely, as anyone who has broken the proverbial bad egg knows to his cost. Nevertheless, we cannot really use it as a means of passing information from one person to another as the dog can. Instead, our eyes and ears have become developed to an almost incredible extent.

THE STRUCTURE OF THE EAR

The ear is really not one sense organ, but two. These have two quite different functions. One of them, of course, is hearing. The other is the detection of rotation and tilting of the head. First of all, however, we shall talk about hearing, the sense which we usually associate with the ear. There are, in fact, three parts to

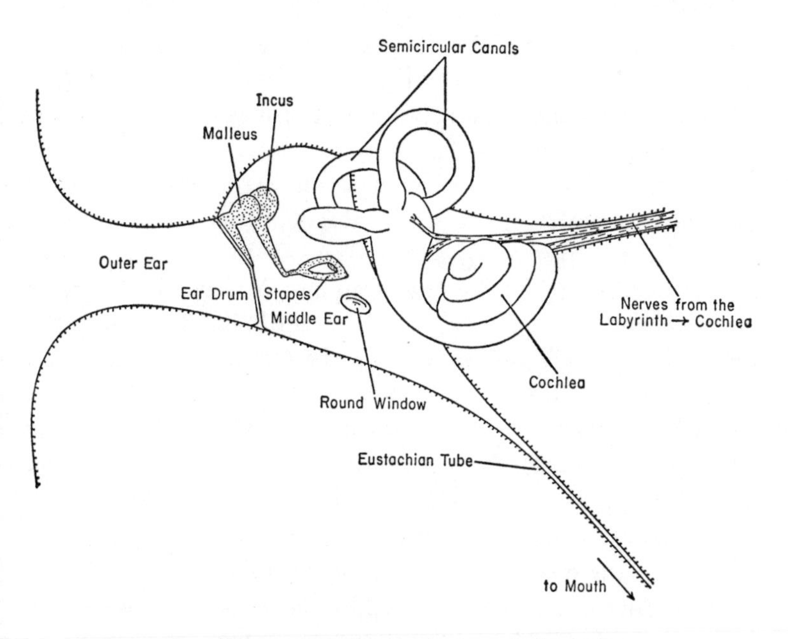

▶ FIGURE 8–1. General plan of the ear.

the ear: outer, middle, and inner. The outer part is simply the hole in the side of your head which is a dead end. Across this end is stretched a thin membrane, the ear drum. On the other side of this membrane is the middle ear, which, like the outer ear, contains air. The inner ear is completely enclosed in bone. The cochlea, which is the part concerned with hearing, consists of a spiral passage hollowed out of the skull. It is divided into three compartments by two membranes which stretch across it. They pass almost, but not quite, up to the very apex. There the two membranes come together and the upper and lower compartments communicate with each other and the middle compartment is closed off. The technical names for these three divisions are scala vestibuli, scala media, and scala tympani, but I think you will find the description easier to follow if we simply call them upper, middle, and lower.

Between the outer and middle ear there is one membrane, the ear drum. Between the middle and inner ear there are two, across the round and oval windows. These separate the air in the middle ear from the inner ear which contains fluid. The oval window membrane closes the upper compartment, and the round window membrane the lower one. Now, since the cochlea is the actual region of the ear which picks up the sound, there must be a system for transferring the sound vibrations from the outer to the inner ear. The passage of sound from air to a liquid presents several problems which we cannot go into. You will have to take my word for it that they are solved beautifully. A sound causes the ear drum to vibrate. Attached to the drum is the malleus, the first of the three tiny bones which are found in the middle ear. The vibrations are transmitted to the other two bones, first the incus and then the stapes. Stapes is the Latin word for stirrup, and if you have ever seen one of these little bones you will know what an accurate description this is. The footpiece of the stapes fits neatly into the oval window. Whenever the ear drum vibrates, the tiny movements are transferred by this system of bony levers to the membrane which closes the oval window. The vibrations are then passed on to the fluid in the upper compartment. They go round to the lower compartment and move the membrane closing the round window. The presence of the round window means that the vibrations of the oval window do not cause marked pressure changes in the inner ear. Its membrane can bulge out into the middle ear and so cushion the shock. You may perhaps have noticed that, as so far described, the middle ear is a closed air space. When going down in a lift we have all felt queer sensations in our ears. These occur because the atmospheric pressure increases as we descend and forces the ear drum inward. The reverse happens when we take off in an aircraft. This time the pressure outside decreases while the pressure in the middle ear remains the same. Our ear drums bulge outward and again make us feel uncomfortable. Fortunately, there is a way for equalizing the pressure on the two sides of the ear drum. There is a very narrow passage which leads from the middle ear to the back of the mouth. It has a long name, the Eustachian tube. Normally it is closed at the mouth end, and the middle ear then really is a closed cavity. When we swallow or suck sweets, however, the tube is opened and air rushes either in or out. The pressure on the two sides of the ear drum is equalized and we feel much more comfortable. When next you fly, and the air hostess hands round sweets to suck, just think of the work your Eustachian tube is doing to keep you more comfortable.

THE COCHLEA

So far, we have not got down to the real mechanism of hearing. The processes we have talked about are only the preliminaries which enable the sound to set the fluid in the inner ear vibrating. We shall now have to learn a little more about the structure of the inner ear. The most important regions are those associated with the lower of the two partitions, the basilar membrane. Lying on this membrane are a number of cells which have stiff hairs sticking out from their upper ends. These hair cells receive the

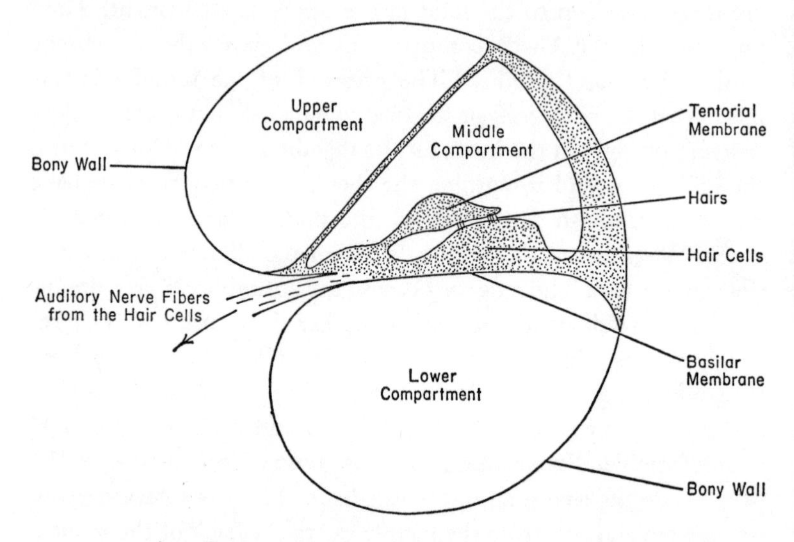

▶ FIGURE 8–2. Cross section of the cochlea.

endings of the sensory neurons of the auditory nerve. On top of the hair cells, throughout the length of the cochlea, lies the tentorial membrane. The tips of the stiff hairs are firmly embedded in this membrane. Apart from this, there is no connection between the tentorial membrane and the underlying cells.

The fluid in the inner ear responds to a sound by vibrating. This, in turn, sets the basilar membrane vibrating. The position where the membrane moves most is related to the frequency of the sound. When a pig squeals, this position is to be found near the base of the cochlea, When a heavy gun booms out, the greatest vibration occurs near the apex. High-frequency sounds have their greatest effect at the lower end; as the frequency of the sound decreases, the position of maximum movement gradually passes toward the apex. At this point, it might be useful for us to make a clear distinction between frequency and loudness. The frequency of a sound determines which part of the membrane is going to vibrate most. The loudness of a sound determines how great that vibration is going to be. A small sound will move only a small part of the membrane; a loud one of the same frequency will cause a much longer part of the membrane to vibrate. The position of maximum vibration, however, will remain the same in both cases.

How is this vibration of the basilar membrane transformed into nervous impulses? When the basilar membrane moves, the hair cells will be moved up and down with it. The tentorial membrane will not move in quite the same way, and since the hair tips are embedded in it, a strain will be put on those hairs. This causes impulses to fire off in the sensory neurons which pass to the cells. The rate of impulse production is proportional to the amount of strain put on the hairs. Since the strain will be greatest where the basilar membrane is vibrating most, the frequency of the sound will be indicated by the auditory nerve fibers which are firing fastest. Just how fast they are firing will indicate the loudness of a sound. Once again we could only build up an accurate picture of the sound by looking at the pattern of discharge in a number of sensory fibers. It is not enough to know how fast an individual neuron is firing. We must also know which of a number of neurons is firing most rapidly.

There has been a great deal of argument about the way in which the hair cells generate impulses in the auditory neurons. Suppose we placed a recording electrode on the round window of a cat's ear, and spoke into that ear. We should be able to pick up fluctuations in potential. If we amplified these potential fluctuations and played them through a loud speaker in another room, people in that room would be able to hear our words. The cat's ear has transformed our voice into electrical changes so accurately that when these changes are put through the appropriate amplification system we can actually hear the words we said. These potential changes can be of all sizes, have no refractory period, and can summate with one another. We are obviously not picking up action potentials in the auditory nerve.

We could further investigate these potentials by exploring the different parts of the cochlea with fine microelectrodes. We would find that they seemed to originate in the hair cells. With low frequency sounds, the biggest changes would be from the hair cells near the apex; with high frequency sounds, they would be found near the base of the cochlea. Suppose we have a high frequency sound. Three distinct phenomena will have their greatest intensities near the base of the cochlea. The basilar membrane will vibrate most in that region. The sensory neurons in that region will discharge faster than the neurons from other parts. The graded potential changes will be most intense there. It would be very strange if this were just coincidence. It seems much more likely that these three things are closely connected. The generally accepted view is that the vibrations of the basilar membrane put a strain on the hair cells which, by an unknown means, produce the graded potential changes. When these potential changes are great enough, the sensory neuron membrane potentials are reduced to threshold and impulses are fired off. Just as with other sense organs we have two distinct electrical stages. First of all a graded, nonconducted potential is produced. If this is sufficiently large it fires off an all-or-nothing impulse in the sensory neuron. In the ear there are a lot of complicating factors which the experts cannot agree about, but when all the arguments are finally over, it will be surprising if the basic pattern is not the same as that in other sensory organs.

It is one of the strange results of evolution that the ear should be an organ both of hearing and balance. The balancing function probably came first in evolution since relatively primitive creatures like fishes have a labyrinth but not a cochlea. The labyrinth has two principal parts, the semicircular canals and the otolith organs. The otolith organs work on a principle not unlike that of the statoliths of the medusa which we discussed in Chapter 1. They seem to be concerned with collecting information about the static position of the body. Here we shall be more concerned with the other part of the system, the semicircular canals, which are designed to detect the rotation and tilting of our heads. The semicircular canals are membranous tubes protected, like the cochlea, by bony passages hollowed out of the skull. As implied by the name, each canal is not a complete circle and begins and ends in the fluid-filled sac known as the utricle. At the beginning of each tube there is a dilatation. There are three canals on each side of the body and the three are at right angles to one another. It is very roughly true to say that one canal is in the horizontal plane and two are in the vertical plane. One of the vertical canals points forward at an angle of 45° to the body's median plane. The other points backward at a similar angle. Thus, if we take both sides together, the two horizontal canals are in the same plane and form a pair. Each frontward-pointing vertical canal is in the same plane as the backward-pointing canal on the other side. You are probably very confused by this and we shall probably get on better if we simply consider the working of the two horizontal canals. Both have a dilatation at their front ends and like the others are filled with fluid. Into the dilatation there projects a shelf of tissue known as the cupula. It is only attached at one end and closes off the dilatation rather like a swing door. The cupula is very well supplied with sensory neurons.

You probably have safety belts fitted to your family car. Do you know why this is? You certainly do if you have ever been in a car which has had to stop very suddenly. If you don't have a safety belt, when the car stops you still keep moving and finish up with your head through the windscreen. The reverse happens when the car accelerates very quickly. This time your body seems to want to remain behind and gets pushed back into your seat. When any sort of container suddenly changes speed, the objects inside it which are not firmly fixed tend to continue at the original speed. When you suddenly stop in a car, your body tends to go on. When you sudenly accelerate, your body tends to get left behind.

Do you see where this is leading? The semicircular canals contain fluid which is not firmly fixed. When your head rotates sideways, your horizontal canals rotate with it, but the fluid in them gets left behind. It pushes against the cupula swing door and

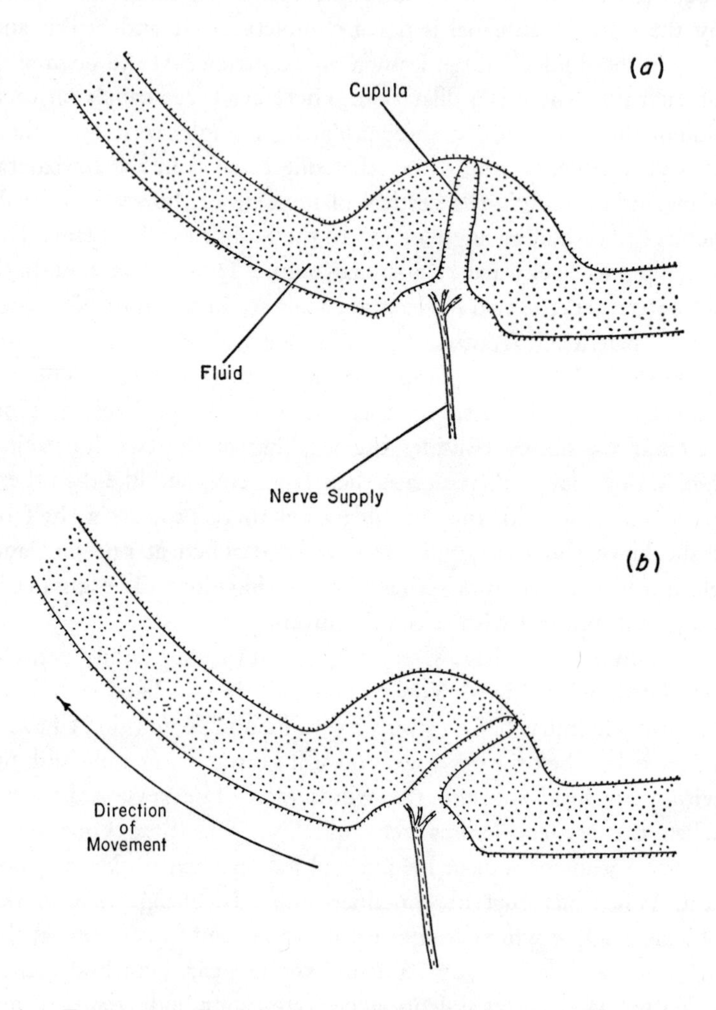

▶ FIGURE 8–3. Semicircular canal mechanism. (*a*) The canal at rest. (*b*) When the canal moves in the direction of the arrow, the fluid is left behind and pushes over the cupula like a swinging door.

bends it over. If, for instance, we turn our head to the right the cupulas in both horizontal canals will be pushed to the left. But because the two canals are on opposite sides, the right cupula will be pushed toward the opening of its canal, while the left one will be pushed away from the opening of the left canal. Pushing the cupula toward the opening has been found to increase the rate of discharge in the sensory neurons. Pushing it away from the opening decreases the rate. So now, when the head turns to the right, the right nerve will increase its discharge rate, while that in the left nerve will decrease. The reverse will happen when we turn to the left. The faster we turn our head, the greater will be the swinging of the cupula and the greater the alteration in discharge. By monitoring the rate of firing in both nerves, our brain can build up a picture of both the direction and the speed of rotation. The other two pairs of canals work in a similar manner and can provide information about movements of the head in any direction. This information is absolutely vital to us if we are to keep our balance. If we human beings did not have semicircular canals we should neither be able to enjoy watching tight-rope walkers at the circus, nor to use bicycles ourselves. We should be completely unable to remain upright. What a strange world it would be!

9 The Eye

Suppose you had a camera and went around clicking the shutter without having a film inside. The lens would be forming beautiful images inside the camera, but you would not get any photographs. In order to obtain a photograph, the image must first be trapped by the film, and then, later on, the film must be taken out of the camera and processed. There are three basic stages in photography: the formation of the image by the lens, the recording of the image by the film, and the processing of the film. Similarly, there are three basic processes in vision. The cornea and lens focus an image on the back of the eyeball. The retina converts this pattern of light into a pattern of nervous impulses. Lastly, the brain interprets these nervous impulses. All three stages are absolutely vital, but here we shall concentrate on the middle one, the way in which the image on the retina is converted into a pattern of nervous impulses.

In order that its energy may be used to fire off a nervous impulse, light must be absorbed. This absorption in the retina is carried out by certain pigments. We can describe the process in very general terms. The pigment is an inert substance which alone cannot generate a nerve impulse. Light falling on to the pigment is absorbed, and the energy splits up the pigment into two substances. One of these is excitatory and is capable of firing off a neuron. If the sensation of light is not to persist long after the light has ceased, the excitatory substance must be quickly destroyed. On the other hand, if the pigment is not to be completely removed in bright light, there must be a system for continually regenerating it. So, in order to transform light into nervous impulses effectively, we must have a pigment which can absorb light and be broken down by it, a system for resynthesizing the pigment, and a system for removing the excitatory product.

The retina consists of an immense number of tiny, tightly packed units designed to detect light. Each one contains pigment. The units fall into two broad groups: the cones which we use in the daytime and which are important in color vision, and the rods which we use at night and which cannot detect color. The rods and cones are so called because of their appearance under the microscope. A remarkable fact, which is not always appreciated, is that the rods and cones point away from the lens. Before it can reach them, the light has to pass through the tangle of nerves and blood vessels which supply the light sensitive units themselves. The explanation for this apparently crazy situation is an evolutionary one and we cannot go into it here.

THE RODS

The rods are better understood than the cones, and we shall begin our description with them. They contain a red pigment, rhodopsin. When light falls upon it, the rhodopsin is split up into retinene and a protein, opsin. The opsin is reactive and can bind ions to itself. It can thus directly alter the ionic concentration inside the rod. In some way, this fires off an impulse in the nerve fiber leading from the rod. The rod is so sensitive that only one molecule of rhodopsin needs to be broken down for a nerve impulse to be produced. The excitatory opsin is removed and the rhodopsin resynthesized by the same mechanism. This is really rather a neat arrangement. There are two pathways for the resynthesis of rhodopsin. Which one is dominant depends on the light situation. In the dark, the retinene and the opsin recombine

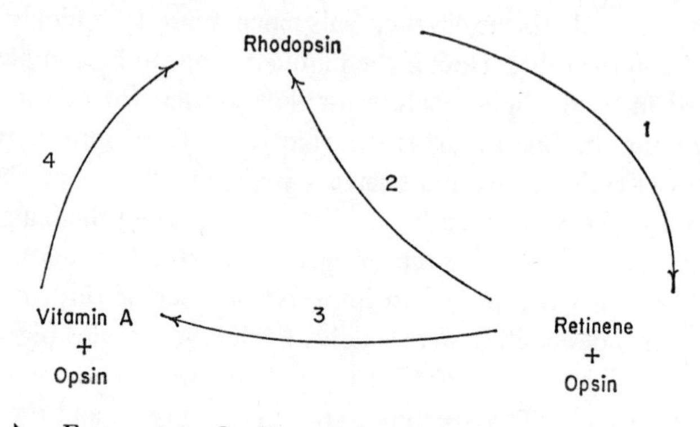

▶ FIGURE 9–1. Outline of chemical processes in the rods.

spontaneously, and this happens if the rhodopsin is split up by a very brief flash of light. The recombination will not take place if the light persists. Under these conditions, the retinene is slowly converted to another compound, vitamin A. In order to regenerate the rhodopsin in this case, retinene must first be formed again from the vitamin A. This takes quite a time. If the rods have been exposed to light for a long period, the original amount of pigment will not be regenerated for about half an hour. Vitamin A, in fact, is essential for night vision as it continually tops up the level of rhodopsin in the rods. You may have heard the story that carrots help you to see in the dark. There is some truth in it because carrots do contain vitamin A and anyone who ate them regularly would be most unlikely to suffer from night blindness.

The sensitivity of the rods to light is not at all constant. When you first go into a cinema and have to sit in the middle of a row, the people at the end of the row curse you. You cannot see their toes, with painful results. After half an hour, a new arrival pushes past you. He treads on your toes. Now it is your turn to curse for you yourself can see your feet quite clearly. During the half hour, your eyes have become accustomed to the darkness, and you can see things which were invisible to you before. The new arrival, who has just come in from the daylight outside, has unadapted eyes and trips over your feet. Being in the dark clearly increases the sensitivity of your eyes. This is because, in the daytime, rhodopsin has been bleached and light can no longer be absorbed by the rods. In the daytime we do not use the rods for seeing. Darkness allows the rhodopsin to be resynthesized, and the eye becomes more and more sensitive. Complete adaptation to dark conditions takes about half an hour. During the last war, night pilots had to wear dark red goggles for 30 minutes before taking off. This allowed their eyes to become adapted and increased their chances of spotting enemy aircraft.

COLOR VISION

Color vision is much more complicated and, like hearing, is a fruitful source of argument. The eye can detect light rays which have wavelengths between about 400 and 700 mμ (one thousandth of a micron). A mixture of all these wavelengths gives a sensation of white light. If the wavelength of the light is about 450 mμ we see blue, if it is about 550 mμ we see green, and if it is about 650 mμ we see red. Intermediate wavelengths produce all the intermediate colors of the spectrum. The people who work theater lights have long known that by mixing red, green, and blue in suitable proportions, almost any color can be reproduced. This fact forms the basis of most theories of color vision.

These theories suggest that there are three types of cone, each containing a different pigment. One pigment is supposed to absorb light in the red region of the spectrum, another in the green region, and the third in the blue region. A sensation of white light results when all three types of cones are stimulated equally. All the other colors result from an unequal stimulation of the three cones. Any color sensation must result from the pattern of activity in a number of neurons. Once again, the rate of discharge in a single neuron cannot give an adequate picture of the situation.

In the retina the neurons coming from both rods and cones

synapse first with a layer of neurons known as the bipolar cells, and these in turn synapse with a layer known as the ganglion cells. The ganglion cells are thus the third neurons in the pathway from the light-sensitive units to the brain. The majority of satisfactory recordings from single units in the retina have come from the ganglion cells. So far it has proved impossible to record clearly the electrical activity of a single rod or cone. The ganglion cell recordings, however, do give some support to the three cone theory. Ganglion cells have been found which respond mainly to red, to green, or to blue light, respectively. Sensitivity curves, showing the way in which these cells respond to different kinds of light, have been plotted. Light with a wavelength of about 570 mμ, for example, causes both the red and the green types of cone to fire. As the wavelength increases, the green type fires more slowly and the red type fires more quickly. As the wavelengths decreases, the reverse happens, and eventually the blue type begins to fire. You can see how by monitoring the pattern of activity in these three types of cell, the brain could determine the color of any light falling on the retina.

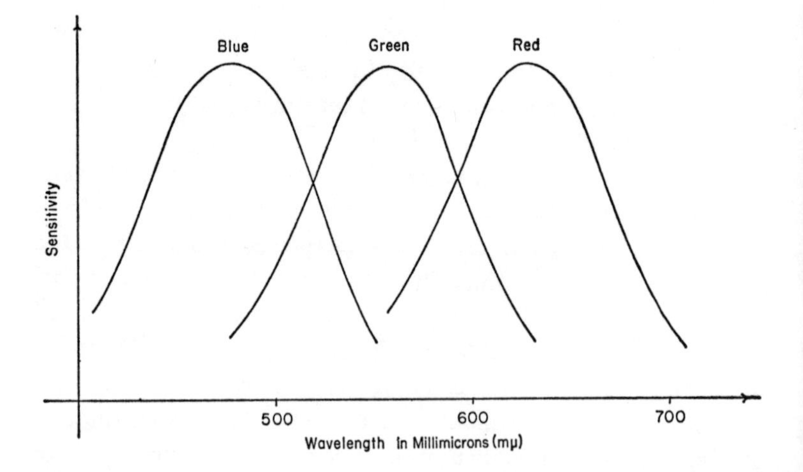

▶ FIGURE 9–2. Diagrammatic representation of the responses of three types of ganglion cell which may help to explain color vision.

Lastly, we must just think briefly of the way in which the retina is organized. The eye is so arranged that, whenever we look at something, the image of that object is focused on a tiny region near the center of the retina known as the fovea. Here, the blood vessels and nerves are kept to the very minimum so that the light can reach the sensitive units with the least possible obstruction. The fovea contains only cones. There are no rods, and so in darkness the fovea will be useless. As one moves away from the fovea toward the edge of the retina, the number of cones decreases while the rods increase. This is why, when we are looking at an object in the dark, we can see it better if we concentrate on a point just to one side. If we concentrate on the object we want to see, the image will fall on the fovea, and we shan't be able to pick up anything. If we look a little to one side, the image of our object will fall on a region of the retina where there are plenty of rods, and we shall be able to see much better.

Here we must end our very brief study of the eye. It is a fascinating subject, and like so many other fascinating subjects is still comparatively unexplored. There is more than enough to occupy any research worker for a lifetime.

10 Controlling the Sensory System

Imagine a perfect summer's day, with the air warm and the sun shining. All the windows and doors of your house are open. Outside on the lawn an elderly relative is sitting in the sunshine trying to go to sleep. In your room you are playing records, and your record player is blaring forth very loudly. Your poor relative cannot go to sleep because of the noise. He becomes more and more irritated until eventually he comes into the house and tells you to be quiet. If we presume that you don't want to annoy him, but still want to play your records, you have two possible choices. You can reduce the noise at its source by turning down the volume control of your record player. Alternatively, you can leave the volume the same but you can shut the doors and windows of your room to prevent the sound escaping into the garden. You can either stop the sound at its source or you can modify it when it has been produced. The body uses both these methods for controlling the information collected by the sensory side of the nervous system. Sometimes it alters the sensitivity of the sense organ itself. Sometimes the sense organ is unaffected but the impulses it produces are controlled as they pass across the synapses on their way to the higher centers of the brain.

First of all, let us think about the first type, in which the sense organ itself is controlled. We have spent some time in discussing the muscle spindle. In Chapter 6 we saw how the spindle is designed to detect length differences between its own special fibers and the main fibers of the muscle. The greater this difference in length, the more strain is put on the nerve endings around the center of the spindle fiber. The rate of discharge of the sensory neurons is proportional to the difference in length between the two sorts of fiber. But the interesting thing is that the spindle fibers are muscle fibers. They are of a rather special sort, it is true, but nevertheless the two ends of the spindle fiber, away from the central sensory region, can contract. If they do contract the spindle will shorten. Even if the main muscle fibers remain the same length and no external stretch is imposed, the sensory neurons will discharge more rapidly. The relative length difference between the main muscle fibers and the spindle fibers has been altered. You can see that in this way it is theoretically possible for the behavior of the sensory receptor to be altered. With the length of the main muscle kept at a constant level, the rate of discharge of the sensory neurons could be modified by contraction of the muscle spindle itself. Is there any experimental evidence to support this idea?

If we were to study a cross section of a muscle nerve we should see that the motoneuron axons fall into two groups, large ones and small ones. The two can be clearly distinguished under the microscope. The large group have diameters in the region of 12μ and the small ones diameters of about 6μ. Now if a graded series of electric shocks is given to a nerve which contains axons of different diameters, the large fibers are stimulated to produce impulses first. Only when the shocks are made stronger are the smaller fibers excited. The larger fibers have a lower threshold to stimulation. On the other hand, if we apply pressure to a nerve, the large fibers are put out of action first. Only when considerable pressure is applied is conduction in the small fibers blocked. These facts were made use of in investigating the control of muscle spindles.

Suppose we set up an experiment in which we can record the tension in a cat's leg muscle. After anesthetizing the animal, we expose the section of the spinal cord which sends neurons to that muscle. We tease a small strand of nervous tissue off the sensory root and so arrange it that we can record from a single sensory neuron from a muscle spindle. We can easily check whether the sensory neuron is coming from a spindle or not. If it is, when the muscle is stretched, the rate of impulse discharge will increase: when the muscle contracts the tension will be taken off the spindle and the rate of discharge will fall. If we were recording from a

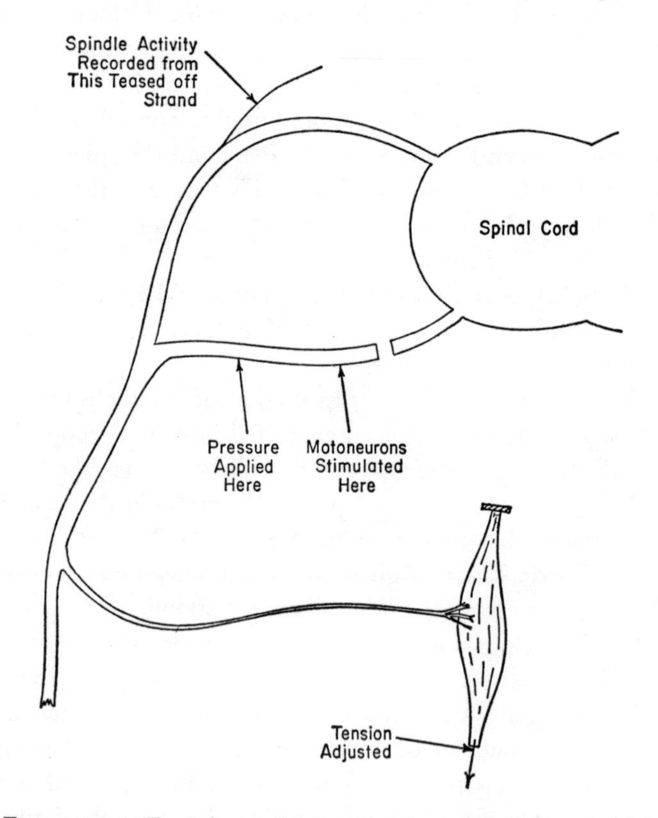

▶ FIGURE 10–1. Experimental set-up to investigate the working of spindle motoneurons.

Golgi tendon organ, the rate of discharge would increase in both cases. We must stretch the muscle slightly at the beginning of the experiment in order to give a steady background rate of spindle discharge. We can then see both reductions and increases in the rate of impulse production. We also want to be able to give a shock to the muscle motoneurons in order to make the muscle contract. If we cut the motor root of the spinal cord and stimulate the cut end away from the cord, we can make the muscle twitch without directly stimulating any sensory neurons at all.

Now, suppose that we give a series of shocks of gradually increasing strength to the motoneuron stump. The large motoneurons, with their low thresholds, will be fired first. Only with strong shocks will impulses be produced in the small motoneurons. When the shock is just strong enough to stimulate the large motoneurons alone, we shall find that the muscle tension is as great as it ever is. If we look at the spindle recording, as the muscle contracts the tension is taken off the spindle, and we see the discharge rate of the sensory neuron decrease. Suppose we now make the shock large enough to fire both large and small motoneurons. The muscle tension will become no greater than it was when only the large motoneurons were firing. The small motoneurons must supply parts of the muscle which are unimportant as far as the strength of the contraction is concerned. The only difference between the two shocks is that, with the large one, there will probably be no decrease in the spindle activity. There may even be an increase. The contraction is the same as before, but this time the tension does not appear to have been taken off the spindles. Perhaps the small motoneurons are causing the spindle muscle fibers to contract (see Figure 13–2).

We can easily test this. We give one of the large shocks to the motoneuron stump, but in between the point of stimulus and the muscle, we apply pressure to the motor root. We adjust this pressure so that it is just great enough to block conduction in the large fibers alone. The only impulses to reach the muscle will now be in the small motoneurons. If we watch the tension record while we give the shock, nothing happens. The muscle fibers supplied by the small motoneurons must be too tiny and weak to make the whole muscle contract. But now look at the record of spindle activity as indicated by the electrode on the sensory root of the spinal cord. When the shock is given, there is a sudden large increase in the discharge rate of the spindle sensory neuron. The conclusion should be obvious to you. The small motoneurons are causing the muscle spindle fibers to contract. The length of the main muscle fibers remains the same, but the muscle spindle is now relatively shorter and so is put under strain. The spindle sensory neurons increase their rate of impulse production. It is a beautiful example of the way in which the working of a sense organ can be controlled.

We shall just look at one more example of the control of sense organ activity. It is a most interesting one but, as yet, not very well understood. Imagine yourself as a small child doing something intensely interesting, like playing in a muddy stream. Your mother calls you, but somehow you do not pay any attention, and you do not go in to wash your hands before your meal. When mother catches you, she scolds you rather severely. In self-defense you say, "But Mummy, I didn't hear you." And, of course, she does not believe a word of it. In fact, it is just possible that you were correct.

As we have seen, the cochlea is designed to pick up sound stimuli and convert them into nervous impulses. We can record these impulses in the auditory nerve as they pass into the brain. In the cat, and possibly in other mammals, there is also a tract of nerve fibers, the bundle of Rasmussen, which runs in the opposite direction from the brain to the cochlea. Suppose we have a steady background noise which produces clear activity in the auditory nerve. Now, while this noise is going on, we stimulate the bundle of Rasmussen. The activity of the auditory nerve falls away. By some unknown mechanism, activity in the bundle of Rasmussen inhibits the production of impulses at the cochlea. Once again the activity of a sense organ is being controlled by the central nervous system. It may be that when you were playing in the stream, your bundle of Rasmussen was active. The sound of your mother's voice no longer caused the discharge of impulses in your auditory nerve. You really did not hear her calling. This, of course, is pure speculation, but it does show what interesting possibilities can be opened up by the control of sense organ activity.

Now we shall turn to the other method of controlling information. The discharge of the sense organ in this case remains unaltered. It is the activity of the neurons which convey impulses up to the higher centers of the brain which is changed. Sensory neurons which collect information about touch and pressure on the skin of the leg enter the spinal cord and pass up it to the lower end of the brain. There, in the region called the gracile nucleus, they synapse with the cell bodies of a second group of neurons. These carry impulses up to the thalamus where they synapse with a third group which passes up to the cerebral cortex. Thus three neurons are needed to carry information about the skin from the leg up to the highest part of the brain. Here, however, we shall be thinking only about the first synapse where the axon of the first sensory neuron reaches the cell body of the second.

The activity of a single one of these cell bodies can be recorded. Many of them have a steady rate of spontaneous discharge. Suppose that we have pushed an electrode into position and we are picking up a spontaneously firing cell. We can then explore the skin by touching it with a pointer. When the pointer touches that part of the skin from which the cell is receiving information, the rate of discharge increases. The part of the skin which gives this response is known as the receptive area of that cell. If the skin just outside the receptive area is touched by the pointer, we may see something which we do not at all expect. The spontaneous discharge of the cell may be decreased. So we can alter the discharge rate of a cell in the gracile nucleus in at least two ways. Stimuli falling within the receptive area increase the rate; stimuli falling just outside this decrease the firing rate.

The magnitude of both effects is proportional to the strength of the stimulus.

Now suppose that we have two cells A and B, whose receptive areas are right next to each other. A touch in the receptive area of A will increase A's rate of discharge and inhibit that of B. A touch in the area of B will produce the reverse effects. What happens when we apply stimuli to both areas at the same time? Imagine that we give a strong stimulus to area A and a weak one to area B, so that twice as many impulses are generated by the sense organs in area A as in area B. Clearly, cell A will discharge much faster than cell B, even if there is no inhibition. What effect will the inhibition have? We said earlier that the degree of inhibition was proportional to the strength of the stimulus. This means that the inhibitory effect of A on B will be much greater than the inhibitory effect of B upon A. Thus the difference between the rates of discharge of the peripheral sense organs will be emphasized in the gracile nucleus neurons. It is a neurophysiological example of the saying of Jesus, "To everyone who has will more be given, and he will have abundance; but from him who has not, even what he has will be taken away."

This is all very well, you may say, but just what is its significance in the life of the animal? Imagine that we now have a third cell C, whose receptive area is in line with those of A and B as shown in the diagram. Suppose that we apply two equal pressure stimuli to A and C. The area of skin B will also be depressed, and sense organs in all three areas will probably discharge. Those in areas A and C should discharge at a slightly faster rate than those in area B, but the difference might not be very great. By looking at the rate of discharge of the first sensory neurons, we might not be able to tell with certainty whether there were two small stimuli, or one large one covering all three receptive areas. If the pattern of sense organ discharge were to be repeated in the cells in the gracile nucleus, this difficulty would continue. But, thanks to the inhibition, the pattern is not repeated and the situation becomes clearer. First of all, look at A and B. The discharge

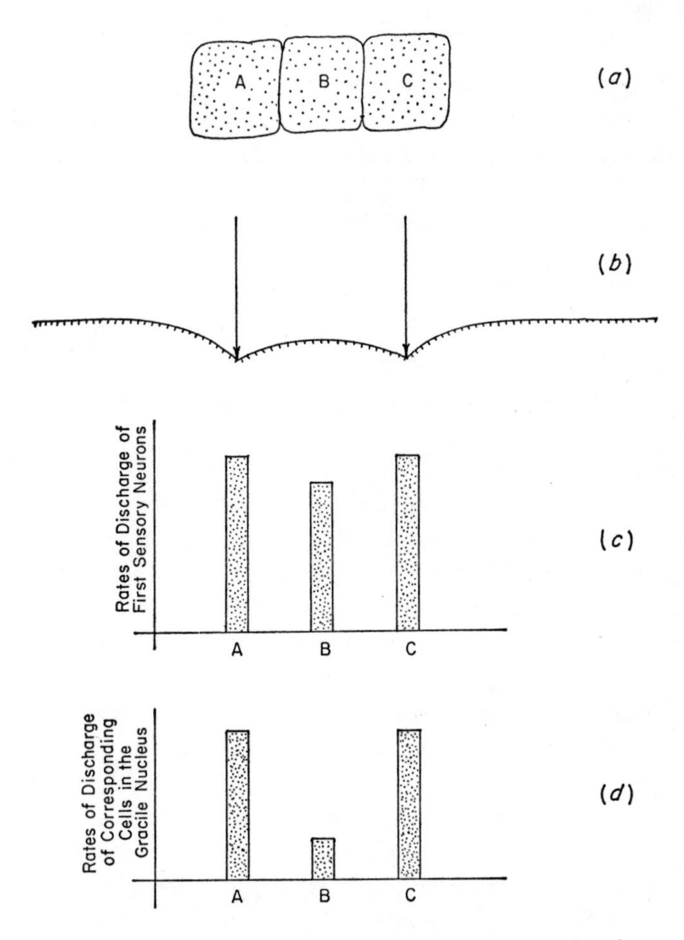

▶ FIGURE 10–2. Simplified diagram illustrating the function of the gracile nucleus. (*a*) Surface view of three receptive fields. (*b*) Two equal stimuli applied to areas A and C. (*c*) The possible response of the first sensory neurons. (*d*) The modification of the response at the cells of the gracile nucleus.

in the sensory neurons coming from area A will be slightly faster than that in the sensory neuron coming from area B. A will therefore have a greater inhibitory effect on B than B will have on A. The slight difference in sensory neuron discharge will be accentuated at the cells in the gracile nucleus. If we look at B and C alone, a similar thing is true. Thus while A and C will each be inhibited only by B, B will be inhibited by both A and C. It will receive a double dose of inhibition. The discharge rate of cell B will be much less than that of cells A and C. There will be no doubt that two stimuli are involved. This is a much simplified account, but the principle is one which is found in many parts of the sensory system. For instance, it is very clearly seen in the sensory pathways leading from the eye and ear. The general effect is to eliminate fuzziness and to make more clear the distinction between two adjacent stimuli.

We have already seen, in the bundle of Rasmussen, a system in which higher centers can inhibit the discharge of a sense organ. This sort of inhibition can also occur at other points along the sensory pathway. For example, the spontaneous discharge of one of the cells in the gracile nucleus can be inhibited by electrically stimulating certain parts of the cerebral cortex. The impulses set off by the stimulation seem to pass downward along a nerve tract which goes to the gracile nucleus. There they inhibit the firing of the cells. This means that a cell in this nucleus may be inhibited in two ways: by impulses coming down from above, and by impulses in adjacent sensory neurons. You are now perhaps beginning to see how very complicated the organization of the nervous system is. When you realize that both sorts of excitatory effects have also been described in the sensory system, you can perhaps understand why progress in neurophysiology seems to be so slow. It will be a long time before the behavior of even the gracile nucleus has been fully worked out.

11 Sleep and Consciousness

The skull contains an enormous mass of nervous tissue. In mammals, the greater part of this is made up by the highest and most recently evolved region of the brain, the cerebral cortex. At any moment, millions of nervous impulses are traveling around this structure. You might expect that with all this electrical activity going on, you should be able, using the right equipment, to detect some potential changes outside the skull. This is in fact possible.

You may have sometimes seen photographs of a man with a large number of wires sticking out from his head. They are wires leading to electrodes. The latter do not actually stick into the skull, but they are firmly attached to the skin of the scalp. Using them it is possible to record potential changes which must be produced by the activity of the immense number of neurons in the cerebral cortex. The potential changes are only very small. They are normally about 50 mV in size, but they are nevertheless easily detectable. This apparatus is now widely used in the diagnosis of brain disease. Its big advantage is that there is no need to actually open the skull. Here, however, we are more interested in the normal working of the brain. For instance, is it possible to detect any differences in brain activity between the waking and sleeping animal? Not surprisingly, it is.

Such a record of potential changes in the cortex is known as an electroencephalogram, or more simply, an EEG. The recording consists of tiny rapid fluctuations in potential which at first sight appear irregular. With experience, it is possible to see some order in the confusion and to realize that these wavelike changes have a predominant frequency (the frequency of a wave is the number of times a complete wave occurs in 1 second). In an alert, awake, adult human being, waves with a frequency of about 10 to 14 per second predominate. On the other hand, in deep sleep, waves of a frequency of 3 per second or even less are seen. As sleep lightens these slow waves are interrupted by short bursts of faster activity. As the person wakes up, these faster waves appear more and more frequently until eventually the whole record is typical of an alert brain.

If only a single neuron were discharging at one time, it would no doubt be impossible to pick up the minute electrical changes by means of electrodes outside the skull. The fact that the recorded activity is rhythmic and not random must mean that large numbers of neurons are firing at precisely the same time. The activity of neurons all over the cerebral cortex seems to be coordinated in some way, enabling all the tiny potential changes to add together and to be recorded outside the skull. The electrical activity of the two sides of the cortex as seen in the EEG still seems to be coordinated even when all nervous tracts which link the two sides are cut. Under these conditions, the two sides of the cerebral cortex clearly cannot communicate directly with each other. They both remain connected to the lower parts of the brain and it may be that a coordinating influence common to the two sides comes up from below.

Coordinated activity of any sort does not usually occur without some outside factor which produces the coordination. A company of soldiers would find it very difficult to march without a band playing or a sergeant major shouting commands. An orchestra would find it impossible to play a symphony without a conductor. A party would be a flop if people were expected to dance without music. Whether it be marching, dancing, or anything else, coordinated activity is almost always associated with something which, as it were, calls out the time. Similarly, something must be calling out the time for the coordinated waves of electrical activity which we can observe in the cerebral cortex. Something must be controlling the changes which occur when we fall asleep and when we wake up again. The experiment of cutting the tracts of nervous tissue linking the two halves of the cerebral cortex strongly suggests that it is some lower region of the brain which provides the coordinating influence.

If the EEG of a sleeping animal is being recorded, and the animal is pricked, the animal wakes up and the EEG pattern changes. This is not very startling. Everyone knows that a sudden stimulus, whether it be a pinprick or a sharp noise, tends to wake up a sleeping person. It does, however, give a clue as to one of the factors which control the EEG. This is the input of sensory information. Whenever we are trying to go to sleep, we do our best to cut down the sensory information which we are picking up. We draw the curtains, switch out the light, and close our eyes to cut out visual information. We shut the bedroom door and turn off our bedside radio to cut out auditory information. We wouldn't dream of trying to go to sleep with loud music blaring out into the room. We wrap ourselves up in warm bedclothes and lie very still to cut out sensory stimulation from our body surface. It is only when we have cut out as much sensory stimulation as possible that we can go to sleep. Even then, a sudden light flash, a car door slamming outside, or simply a very hot or a very cold night can prevent us going to sleep. Clearly the input of sensory information is an extremely important factor in controlling the level of consciousness.

THE RETICULAR FORMATION

As we have already seen, sensory impulses from the skin can reach the higher centers of the brain by a fairly direct pathway involving three neurons. It is possible that this pathway could be concerned in controlling the level of consciousness. Fortunately, in the lower part of the brain, the second-stage neurons of this pathway are all closely grouped together. It is possible to cut through this tract of nervous tissue in an animal and thus to block this route up to the cerebral cortex. We might expect now that pricking a sleeping animal would not wake it up. In fact, the animal behaves just as before. A prick converts the EEG from the sleeping to the waking pattern. We must look for another route whereby sensory information can travel up to the cerebral cortex.

In Chapter 7, we discussed the possibility of passing long needles through the brain without causing much obvious damage to the animal. These needles can either be used for injecting substances or for electrical stimulation. There is a region, also in the lower part of the brain, known as the reticular formation. If a needle is passed into this area and used for electrical stimulation, remarkable alterations can occur in the EEG. Stimulation can wake up an animal and alter the EEG from the slow sleeping pattern to the fast waking one. If the upper part of the reticular formation is damaged, the animal remains in a permanent coma. It cannot be aroused either by electrical stimulation or by ordinary sensory stimuli such as pricks or loud noises. The animal remains in this state even if the main, three neuron sensory pathways remain intact. The conclusion seems clear: there must be another route through the reticular formation whereby sensory information can reach the cortex. It is probably this route which controls the level of consciousness.

The idea that sensory impulses reach the reticular formation can be confirmed by recording from single neuron cell bodies in the region. If we were to do such an experiment, say on a cat, we should be able to find cells which responded to every conceivable type of sensory stimulation. Some would increase their discharge rate when the skin was pricked, some when a joint was moved. Some would fire faster in the presence of noise, some when a light was shone into the animal's eye. All types of sensory impulses seem to reach this part of the brain. If a large amount of information is coming in, the animal tends to be alert, and the EEG is of the fast pattern. If there is only a little sensory stimulation, the animal tends to become drowsy, the EEG becomes slower and slower, and eventually the creature goes to sleep. The reticular formation seems to collect the sensory information and then, using it, to control the level of cortical activity.

SIFTING THE INFORMATION

But the situation is not quite so simple as might seem at first sight. The reticular formation does not take notice only of the amount of information coming in; it is also concerned with the type. Anyone who, for the first time, tries to sleep near a large clock tower is aroused every quarter of an hour throughout the night and is very bad-tempered when he gets up in the morning. Yet if that person goes to live near the clock tower, he will soon sleep soundly all night. The reticular formation has become accustomed to the sound. The volume is the same, but the system now realizes that the sound is unimportant and there is no need to arouse the cortex. Yet if the bedroom door creaks while the clock is striking, the person will immediately wake up. The reticular formation picks up this tiny unusual noise, says, as it were, "This is important," and arouses the cortex. The system therefore does not merely respond to the quantity of information coming in. It sifts and selects the information, only arousing the cortex if something unusual, and therefore possibly important, happens.

A similar thing can be demonstrated in an animal. Suppose that we are recording from a part of the reticular formation which receives impulses from the ear, and we produce a series of loud noises. For the first few times, there will be a large response in the neurons of that region. If the sound is steadily repeated, however, the rate of discharge becomes less and less, and the response may even disappear completely. For the first few times, the sound is unusual and therefore important. There is a large response. Gradually, however, the neurons begin to behave as though they were becoming accustomed to the stimulus. Their response becomes smaller and eventually fades away.

The reticular formation is probably also concerned with directing the attention of an animal which is already awake. One of the ways in which this is done may perhaps be by suppressing information coming in by irrelevant pathways. The first synapse on the auditory pathway is in the cochlear nucleus. Here the neurons coming from the ear synapse with the cell bodies of the next set of neurons. It is possible to record the activity of these cells. In a relaxed cat, a series of clicks produces a series of large, clear, potential changes in the cochlear nucleus. If the clicks then continue, while the cat's attention is attracted by a mouse or by a fishy smell, the response of the cochlear nucleus is considerably reduced. As soon as the attention is directed to a particular subject, irrelevant auditory information is cut out. The animal concentrates on the mouse or the fish. The situation is a familiar one and there are many examples which can be shown without the need for complicated apparatus. For example, how many times have you cut yourself when playing a game and realized it only when the game was over? Your attention was concentrated on playing, and minor irrelevant stimuli such as mild pain were not noticed. Or, while sitting in class, how many times has your attention wandered to thinking about what you were going to do when school was over? Then the teacher has asked you a question. The first time you did not even hear it and you realized what was happening only when your classmates began to laugh. Your attention was elsewhere, and you just did not hear the teacher at all.

I am sure that you can think of many more examples for yourself. The few we have talked about in this chapter may help you to realize how important the reticular formation is. It is a very complicated part of the brain and, as in so many fields, we are now only just beginning to understand the way it works.

12 Jumping the Gaps

At the close of the nineteenth century, a great argument was being fought out. The point at issue was the structure of the nervous system. One group claimed that all the neurons were directly connected with one another, that there was no actual gap between one neuron and the next. The other group said that each neuron was separate and distinct, there was a tiny but definite gap between two adjacent neurons. Thanks largely to the work of a brilliant Spanish histologist, Ramon y Cajal, the second group won. Everyone now believes that, at least in mammals, all the neurons are completely separate from each other. The gap between two adjacent neurons is called a synapse.

Most neurons are made up of a cell body, a number of small processes called dendrites, and a long process called the axon. Impulses usually begin in the cell body and then travel outward along the axon. The whole of the cell body, except for the part where the axon begins, is covered with the endings of axons from other cells. The gaps between these axon endings and the cell body are the synapses.

Suppose now that we have an impulse which is traveling along an axon as described in Chapter 3. What happens when this impulse reaches the end of the axon? How does the activity cross the synapse from the axon ending to the cell body of the next neuron? People used to think that the electric currents generated by the impulse in the axon crossed the gap and excited the next cell electrically. Gradually, however, a large amount of evidence built up which suggested that this was not so. A crucial point was the delay which was always observed when an impulse passed from one neuron to the next. The impulse always took about half a millisecond to cross the gap. Now a millisecond is a thousandth of a second, and no doubt this seems to you to be a very short delay. Nevertheless, electricity travels at the speed of 186,000 miles per second. In half a millisecond an impulse which was being conducted like electricity in a wire could travel about 90 miles. If all the processes involved were electrical the delay would be much shorter than it really is.

Nowadays we believe that there is a completely different mechanism. In the endings of an axon are stored minute globules of a chemical. When an impulse comes along, some of these globules are released from the ending. The chemical then diffuses across the gap and acts upon the cell membrane of the next neuron. It alters the ionic permeability of that membrane. Ions can pass more freely in and out of the cell body, and this will alter the membrane potential. If the membrane potential reaches the threshold value, an impulse will be fired off. Much of the work on the way in which the impulse releases the chemical has been done on the neuromuscular junction. We shall be discussing this more fully in Chapter 15. Here we shall be thinking mainly about the way in which the chemical affects the cell membrane. What exactly happens when a chemical crosses a synapse and reaches the next neuron?

We have seen that with nerve conduction and sensory reception, little progress was made until someone devised a method for recording from inside a neuron. Precisely the same thing happened in the study of synapses. The chief difficulty is that almost all cell bodies are in the central nervous system. You can easily understand that it is relatively simple to isolate a single axon or sense organ in the outer regions of the body. To push a microelectrode into a single cell body in a mass of nervous tissue presents a formidable task.

The problem was solved in Australia by Sir John Eccles. The nerve cells whose axons transmit impulses to muscles are called motoneurons. When motoneuron impulses reach a muscle they cause the muscle fibers to contract. Eccles made use of the fact that the motoneurons which supply a particular muscle tend to be collected together in the spinal cord. Their cell bodies are very large, and the solution to the problem was, in theory, fairly simple. When Eccles wished to record from a motoneuron which supplied a particular muscle, he simply pushed a microelectrode very slowly through that section of the spinal cord until it pierced a cell. This was clearly indicated because the potential recorded by the electrode suddenly fell from 0 to about —70mV. The chief problem posed by the technique is the difficulty of keeping the tip of the microelectrode inside the cell. The slightest movement of either the animal or the electrode will prevent this. There must be apparatus for holding both the spinal cord and the electrode absolutely rigid. It may mean building a special room where vibrations due to traffic and machinery are kept to an absolute minimum. These problems have now been solved in many laboratories. By this remarkable method Eccles himself was able to investigate the way in which the chemical released by the axon endings on the cell body altered the motoneuron membrane potential.

Before he could proceed, he had to have a reliable method of causing the release of the chemical. In order to do this he made use of some well-known facts which we must briefly discuss. Suppose that you bend your knee. If you feel the surface of your leg while you are doing this, you will find that a surprisingly large number of muscles are involved. They are mainly on the back of your thigh. All the muscles there help one another in bending the knee, and they are known as synergists. Now suppose that you do the opposite and straighten your knee as much as possible. This time it is mainly the muscles on the front of the thigh which are involved. The movement is clearly the reverse of bending your leg. The muscles which pull the lower part of your leg back are said to be antagonistic to those which straighten your leg. Muscles which help each other to carry out a particular movement are synergists. Those which carry out opposite movements are antagonists. If antagonistic muscles contracted at the same time as one another, they would work against one another.

We have already discussed the way in which the sensory neurons which supply muscle spindles are fired when the muscle is stretched. We have not talked about the way in which these neurons end in the spinal cord. In fact, each neuron breaks up into several branches. The main ones pass to the motoneurons of the same muscle. Stretching a muscle, therefore, causes the motoneurons which supply that muscle to discharge impulses. The muscle contracts. Subsidiary branches of the sensory neuron pass to the motoneurons of synergistic muscles. By themselves, these subsidiary branches will not cause the synergistic motoneurons to discharge. Stretching one muscle will not usually cause its synergists to contract. It will, however, mean that the synergistic motoneurons will be more easily excited. This may be because of an effect on the membrane potentials of these motoneurons.

We can easily demonstrate this synergism by a simple experiment. If you look at a friend who is standing on tiptoe, you will see two bulges side by side on his calf. These bulges are due to the contraction of the lateral and medial gastrocnemius muscles. Both these muscles have the same action; they straighten out the ankle joint. They help each other to do this and so they are synergists. Each muscle has its own nerve which can be dissected out and cut. These nerves are mixed; they contain both sensory neurons going to the spinal cord from the muscle and motoneurons coming out of the spinal cord and going to the muscle. As we saw in Chapter 2, these two sorts of neurons separate just before the spinal cord. The sensory ones pass into the back of the cord and the motoneurons come out at the front.

Now if we gave a shock to the nerve to lateral gastroc-

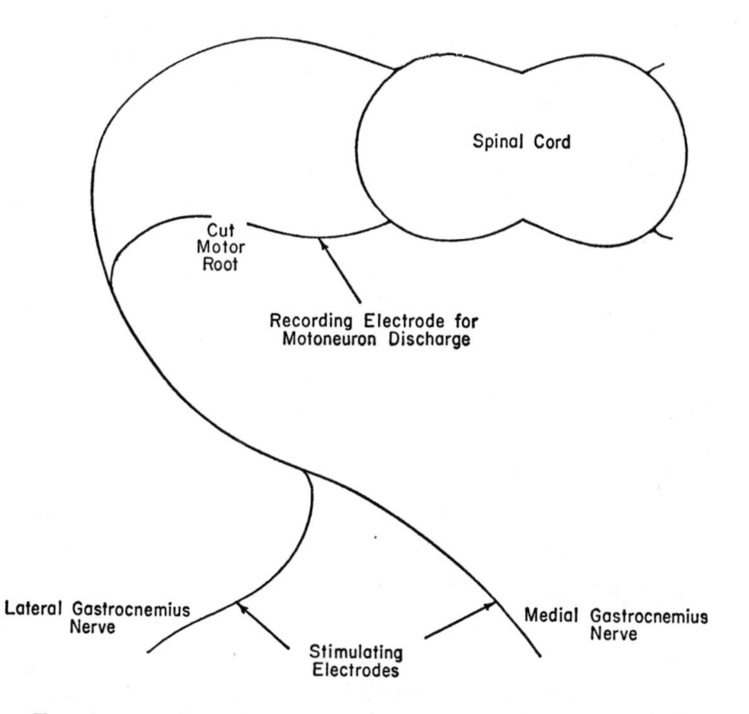

▶ FIGURE 12–1. Experimental set-up to show facilitation of synergistic motoneurons.

nemius, both sorts of neuron would be fired off. When axons are stimulated electrically in this way, impulses pass in both directions from the point of stimulation. With the nerve dissected out, in a sensory neuron one impulse would pass in the normal direction up to the spinal cord; another would pass in the "wrong" direction and peter out at the cut end. With the shock to the mixed nerve we should also stimulate motoneurons. One impulse passing in the usual direction toward the muscle would also peter out at the cut nerve end. The other impulse would pass backward up to the spinal cord and would fire the cell body of the motoneuron in the wrong way. Now we are interested in the firing of motoneurons by impulses in sensory axons. If our experiment is not to be ruined, we must prevent the motoneurons from being fired backward. This is very simple. All we need do is to cut the motor root coming from the front of the spinal cord. Now if we give a shock to the lateral gastrocnemius nerve, impulses will pass up to the spinal cord in the sensory neurons and will, in turn, cause the motoneurons to fire. The motoneuron impulses can be recorded in the stump coming from the front of the spinal cord. Because the motor root has been cut, impulses passing the wrong way up the motoneurons will not interfere with the record. This preparation can be used to give some very interesting results.

The crude record which can be obtained by putting electrodes on the stump of the motor root is due to the summation of the individual impulses in single motoneurons. If only a few motoneurons are discharging the sum of the action potentials will be small; if many are discharging, the sum will be large. Thus the size of the recorded potential change will be proportional to the number of motoneurons which are firing.

Now suppose that we give a shock to the lateral gastrocnemius nerve and adjust the strength of the stimulus so that the record in the motoneuron stump is only small. Suppose that we also do the same thing with the medial gastrocnemius nerve. What will happen if, instead of giving the two shocks separately, we now give them together? We might think that the record would be equal in size to the sum of the two individual records, but we would be wrong. In fact, the record which results from the two shocks being given simultaneously is much larger than this. Why should this be? The single shocks succeed in actually firing only a few motoneurons. These shocks do, however, increase the excitability of a large number of synergistic motoneurons. When both shocks are given together, the motoneurons fired by the single shocks again discharge. In addition, the summation of the two effects on synergistic motoneurons fires off impulses in a large number of extra cells. The record is much larger than would be expected if we just added together the effects of the single shocks.

A very different picture emerges if antagonistic muscle nerves are used for the experiment. Suppose one test shock is given to the lateral gastrocnemius nerve and the size of the record in the motor root noted. We could then give shocks to one of the antagonistic muscle nerves on the front of the leg. Suppose that we adjusted the strength of the shock to this nerve until it just failed to produce a response in the motor root. What would happen if we gave this apparently subthreshold shock simultaneously with our standard lateral gastrocnemius shock? You probably expect that the response would be smaller than before. Actually it is precisely the same size. But now let us give the antagonistic shock about half a millisecond before the other. This time the record will be much smaller and it may even vanish altogether. Sensory impulses from one muscle can therefore inhibit the discharge of antagonistic motoneurons.

Thus, when Eccles began his experiments on recording from inside motoneurons, he had several facts to try to account for. The main ones were as follows:

(1) Sensory impulses from muscle spindles make the motoneurons which supply synergistic muscles more excitable.

(2) The same sensory impulses inhibit the responses of antagonistic motoneurons.

(3) The increase in exitability occurs immediately, but the inhibitory impulse must be fired off half a millisecond before the excitatory one if it is to be effective.

Eccles therefore inserted his microelectrode into a motoneuron supplying a particular muscle and then gave test shocks to both synergistic and antagonistic muscle nerves. When he gave a shock to a synergistic muscle nerve, the membrane potential of the motoneuron was always reduced. With a small test shock it might be reduced only a few millivolts, say from −70 to −65mV. With increasing stimulus strength, the membrane potential tended to be reduced further and further. Eventually the threshold was reached and the motoneuron fired off. You can now see why sensory impulses from a muscle increase the excitability

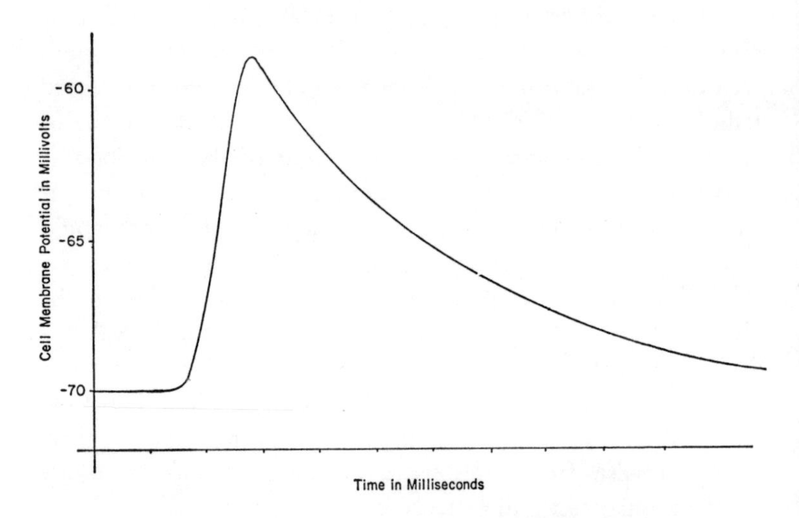

▶ FIGURE 12–2. A typical motoneuron EPSP.

of synergistic motoneurons. They lower the membrane potentials of those motoneurons. This reduces the gap between the resting potential and the threshold for firing. The motoneuron can then be more easily discharged. Eccles called the potential change toward threshold the excitatory postsynaptic potential or EPSP.

The opposite situation occurred when antagonistic muscle nerves were stimulated. This time the motoneuron membrane potential was increased to a level higher than the resting potential. The difference between the resting potential and the threshold for firing was therefore increased. This clearly means that in this situation the motoneuron will be less excitable. This increase in membrane potential was appropriately called the inhibitory postsynaptic potential or IPSP. You can see that Eccles' work provided an explanation in terms of membrane potentials of the changes in motoneuron excitability which we noted in our experiment. Synergistic stimuli, which increase excitability, lower the cell membrane potential toward threshold. Antagonistic stimuli, which reduce excitability, raise the membrane potential away from the threshold.

If you have read the earlier chapters carefully you may have noticed some similarity between the production of an impulse at a sense organ and the production of an impulse at a motoneuron. In the sense organ, the first event is a nonconducting potential which can be graded in size and which can summate with other similar potentials. It is produced by an increase in the permeability of the sensory ending to all ions. If this so-called generator potential is large enough, it can cause an impulse to be fired off in the adjacent part of the axon. This impulse is of constant size, is rapidly conducted, and cannot summate with other impulses. This means that in a sense organ there are two sorts of membrane associated with two very different types of potential change. The firing of a motoneuron is remarkably similar. The chemical released at the synapse produces a potential change which can vary in size, and which can summate with other similar potentials on the same cell body. If enough synapses are activated, the cell resting potential is reduced to threshold and an all-or-nothing impulse is produced and passes out along the axon. Many experiments have now confirmed that the excitatory potential is usually caused by an increase in permeability to all ions. This, of course, as you will remember, tends to reduce the membrane potential to zero. You can now see how extraordinarily similar are the excitatory processes at motoneurons and sense organs. In both cases a variable, nonconducting potential change precedes the generation of an all-or-nothing impulse. In both cases two very different types of membrane are found. As we shall see later when we look at muscle, this seems to be a general property of excitable tissues.

In motoneurons, and probably at most synapses, there is an additional complication. There are two distinct sorts of variable potential changes, the IPSP's and the EPSP's. While the EPSP is very similar to the generator potential, the IPSP is rather different. The change in ionic permeability during inhibition tends to make the inside of the cell body about 80mV negative to the outside. This is probably mainly due to an increase in permeability just to potassium and chloride ions. Thus in excitation and inhibition, the

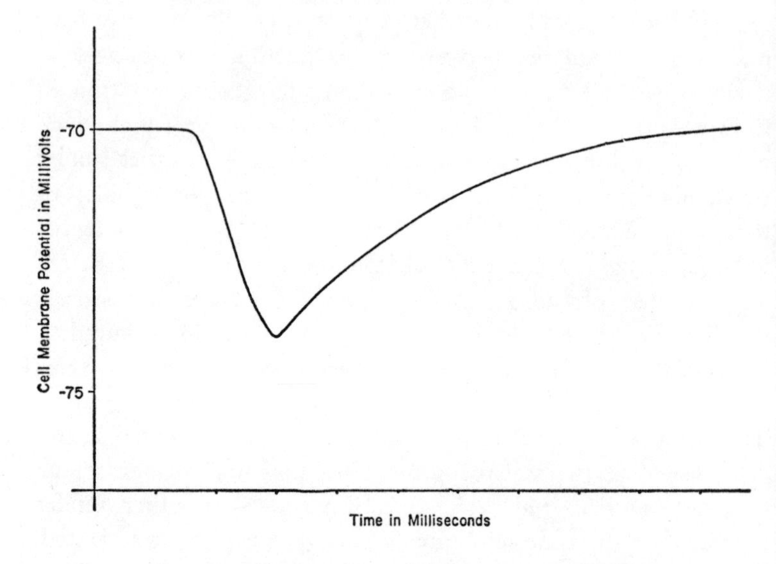

▶ Figure 12–3. A typical motoneuron IPSP.

permeability changes are very different. As you can no doubt imagine, it is unlikely that both these effects are produced by the same chemical. There are probably two chemicals released at a motoneuron; one produces excitation and the other produces inhibition. When there is more of the excitatory material the cell fires off. When there is more of the inhibitory one it does not.

So far we have still left one fact unexplained and that is the delay required to produce inhibition. Why must an inhibitory stimulus be fired into the dorsal root half a millisecond before an excitatory one in order to produce its effect? It is a consequence of the fact that each neuron seems to release only one type of synaptic chemical. Much of the chemical is probably produced in the cell body. From there it diffuses along the axon and into all its branches. You can imagine what might happen if two chemicals, one excitatory and one inhibitory, were made in the cell body. It would be very difficult to make sure that the right chemical went down the right branches of the axon.

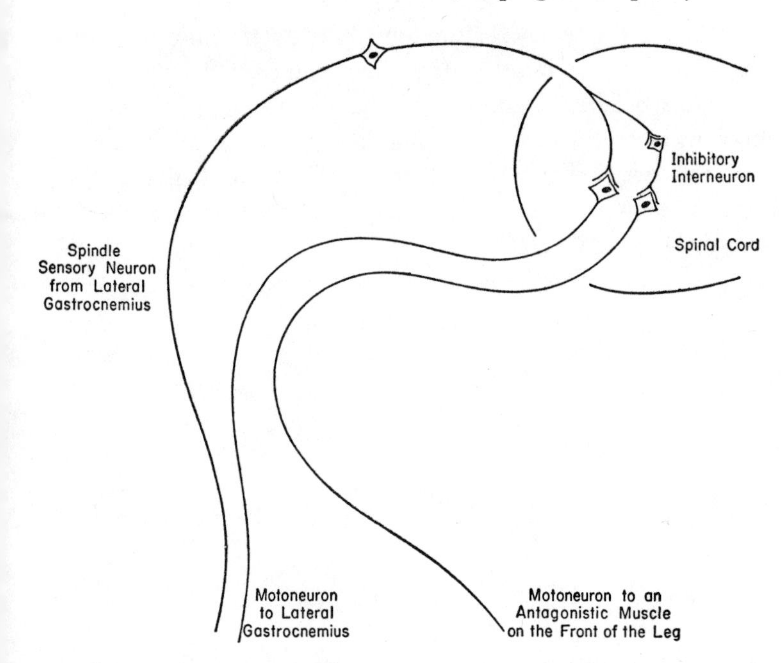

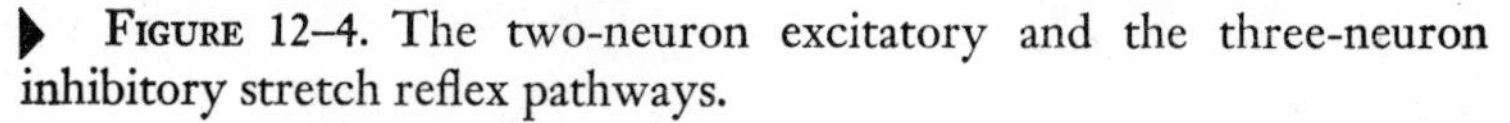
▸ FIGURE 12–4. The two-neuron excitatory and the three-neuron inhibitory stretch reflex pathways.

This problem would clearly be avoided if only one type of transmitter chemical were to be produced by each neuron. All the sensory neurons from muscle spindles produce the excitatory type. How then can a sensory neuron from a muscle inhibit the antagonistic motoneurons? The answer is simple: by having another neuron in the pathway. The spindle neuron excites this second neuron to fire. The second neuron is designed to produce the inhibitory chemical. Its axon branches go to antagonistic motoneurons and inhibit them. The excitatory pathway has only two neurons, the sensory neuron from the spindle and the motoneuron. The inhibitory one has three because of the necessity for changing from an excitatory to an inhibitory chemical. Here lies the explanation for the delay in producing inhibition. There is an extra neuron with an extra synapse in the pathway.

So far the synapses at motoneurons are the only ones which have been studied in great detail, and you may think that this is rather a specialized case. Information about other synapses in the nervous system is now beginning to come in. In most cases, the processes are similar to those just described, and it is very likely that the basic mechanisms of synaptic transmission are the same everywhere.

13 : Reflexes

If you are in your kitchen at home and by accident touch a hot plate or saucepan, you immediately pull your hand away. You do not have to think about it. Your hand is withdrawn automatically. Your body has carried out a reflex action, and in this example we can see all the basic components of this type of activity.

First of all there must be a stimulus, in this case the hot plate. Information about this stimulus must be picked up by a sense organ and conveyed to the central nervous system by a sensory neuron. In the central nervous system there must be a system for carrying the information to the appropriate place. Instructions about the action to be taken are then sent away from the central nervous system along motoneurons. Finally, the appropriate muscles contract, and the arm is drawn away from the hot plate. The fact that all this occurs in an instant is a good indication of how highly developed the nervous system is.

But the reflex we have just described is a very complicated one involving many neurons and muscles. In order to see the basic principles of reflex activity a little more clearly, we must turn to something a little simpler. At some time when you have been to the doctor, he has probably tested your so-called knee jerk. He has either asked you to cross one leg over the other or sat you on a table with your legs dangling. With a little rubber hammer

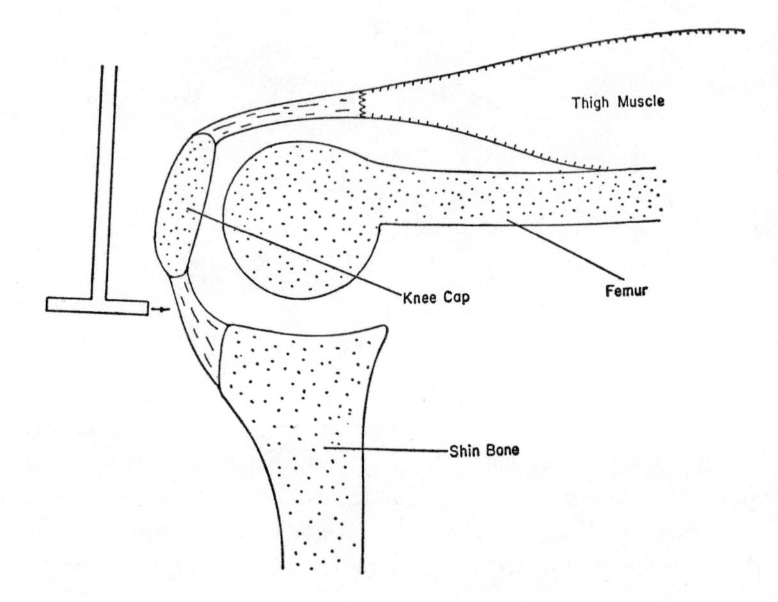

▶ Figure 13–1. The knee jerk. A tap on the tendon just below the knee cap stretches the thigh muscle. In response, the thigh muscle contracts, causing the leg to kick forward.

or with the side of his hand he has tapped you just below the knee and your leg has kicked forward. If you have never seen this done, it is very simple to try it out on yourself.

Why should your leg kick forward if it is tapped just below the knee? In order to understand it, we must first do a little anatomy. On the front of your thigh there is a great mass of muscle which you use for straightening your knee joint. At its lower end, this muscle is attached to some fibrous tissue known as a tendon. This tendon is attached to the upper end of your knee cap. From the lower end of your knee cap, another piece of fibrous tissue goes down to your shin bone. If your knee is bent, when your thigh muscle contracts, it pulls on the tendon and straightens out your leg. Your knee cap is acting as a sort of pulley on the front of your knee joint. It helps to transfer the pull of the muscle to the shin bone. If you put your hand on the front of your thigh when you straighten your leg, you should be able to feel the muscle contracting.

When the doctor taps you just below the knee, he is in fact tapping the tendon as it passes from the knee cap to the shin bone. This sudden tap passes back to the muscle and gives it a tiny sharp stretch. This slightly lengthens the main muscle fibers relative to the spindle fibers. The sensory neurons supplying the spindles increase their rate of discharge. The information is carried up to the spinal cord. There, the sensory neurons synapse with the motoneurons which supply the same muscle. The motoneurons are caused to fire and the muscle gives a sudden twitch, kicking the leg forward. This may give you an idea of how sensitive the muscle spindles are, since the stretch caused by the tap which they detect is only a very small one indeed.

It has long been known that reflex activity can be greatly modified by impulses coming down from higher centers; we shall be discussing this in the next chapter. In order to investigate the reflexes in their simplest, uncomplicated form, it is essential to eliminate this higher control. This can be done most easily by cutting the spinal cord of an experimental animal. If we cut the spinal cord at the lower end of the chest, the front part of the animal will be unaffected and will continue to breathe. The spinal reflexes in the back legs can then be studied, uncomplicated by the activity of the higher control centers.

Before we could do any experiments, we would have to wait a little while for the spinal cord to recover from the shock. When the spinal cord of any animal is cut, for a while the regions of the body supplied by nerves from parts of the cord below the cut are completely paralyzed. Voluntary and reflex activity and conscious sensation are completely absent. The voluntary activity and the conscious sensation never recover. The reflexes, on the other hand, gradually return. In a dog, for instance, which has recovered from this state of shock, pinching the back leg will cause the leg to be pulled away. The dog cannot feel the pinch, nor can it voluntarily direct its muscles to contract. The activity is completely reflex. The interesting thing is that the length of the period of shock after cutting the spinal cord seems to be proportional to the development of the higher centers of the brain. In a frog, the reflexes recover completely within a few minutes and in a dog or a cat within an hour or so. In a man, who has broken his spinal cord in an accident, no reflex activity can be detected for two or three weeks. It is true of any organization that, as the higher control centers become more complex and important, the lower parts of the system lose their independence. In man, the spinal cord has largely lost its ability to act on its own. It takes much longer to recover than does the spinal cord of a frog when the guidance and control of the higher centers are removed.

The stretch reflex, of which the knee jerk is an example, is the simplest form of reflex activity in mammals. In a spinal animal (one with its spinal cord cut) a great deal can be learned by stretching a muscle and recording simultaneously the activity of the sensory neurons as they enter the back of the spinal cord, and of the motoneurons as they emerge from the front. If we keep the muscle under slight tension, we shall get a low level of background activity in both sensory neurons and motoneurons. Now suppose we give a tiny stretch to the muscle. First of all, there is a burst of activity in the sensory root of the cord. Since the stretch was far too small to excite the Golgi tendon organs, we can safely assume that the impulses are mainly in sensory neurons coming from the muscle spindles. Almost immediately, this is followed by a burst of impulses in the motoneurons, and then by a muscle twitch. It is possible to measure the time between the impulses entering the back of the cord and coming out at the front. If we do this, we shall find that it is not much more than half a millisecond. During this time, only one synapse can have been crossed. The information must have been passed directly from the sensory neurons to the motoneurons.

If we keep our eyes on the recording equipment we can learn still more. Immediately the muscle twitches, the activity in the sensory root ceases. The muscular contraction has taken the tension off the spindles, and their sensory neurons no longer discharge impulses. As might be expected, the cessation of sensory activity is at once followed by a cessation of impulses in the motoneurons. This allows the muscle to relax toward its original length. As it does so, the spindles are again stretched at their background level and the muscle is maintained in its original position.

You can perhaps see that as long as the muscle spindle fibers remain the same length, if the muscle is stretched, the stretch reflex will cause it to return to its original length. If the small motoneurons alter the length of the muscle spindle fibers, the stretch reflex will at once cause the length of the main muscle to be altered. Suppose that the small motoneurons fire more rapidly and cause the spindle fibers to contract. Just as with a stretch imposed from outside, the main muscle fibers are now relatively longer than they were before. The spindle neurons fire more rapidly and, in turn, the motoneurons discharge to shorten the main muscle fibers. A new equilibrium position is reached, with the muscle more contracted than it was before. A lengthening of the spindle fibers would produce the opposite effect and by the stretch reflex the main muscle fibers would relax. The muscle spindles play a key role in determining the state of contraction of a muscle. When the spindle muscle fibers contract, the whole muscle contracts; when they relax, the whole muscle lengthens. The principle of the stretch reflex is remarkably similar to that of the thermostat which we discussed in Chapter 4. The muscle spindle is like the temperature setting: when the main muscle fibers are relatively too long, it sets in motion a process to bring them back to the right length. A similar thing happens when the main fibers are relatively too short. It is often surprising how widely this type of control is used.

The stretch reflex is, of course, very simple. Only one synapse is involved. The response is limited to the muscle which received the stimulus, although by careful testing it may be pos-

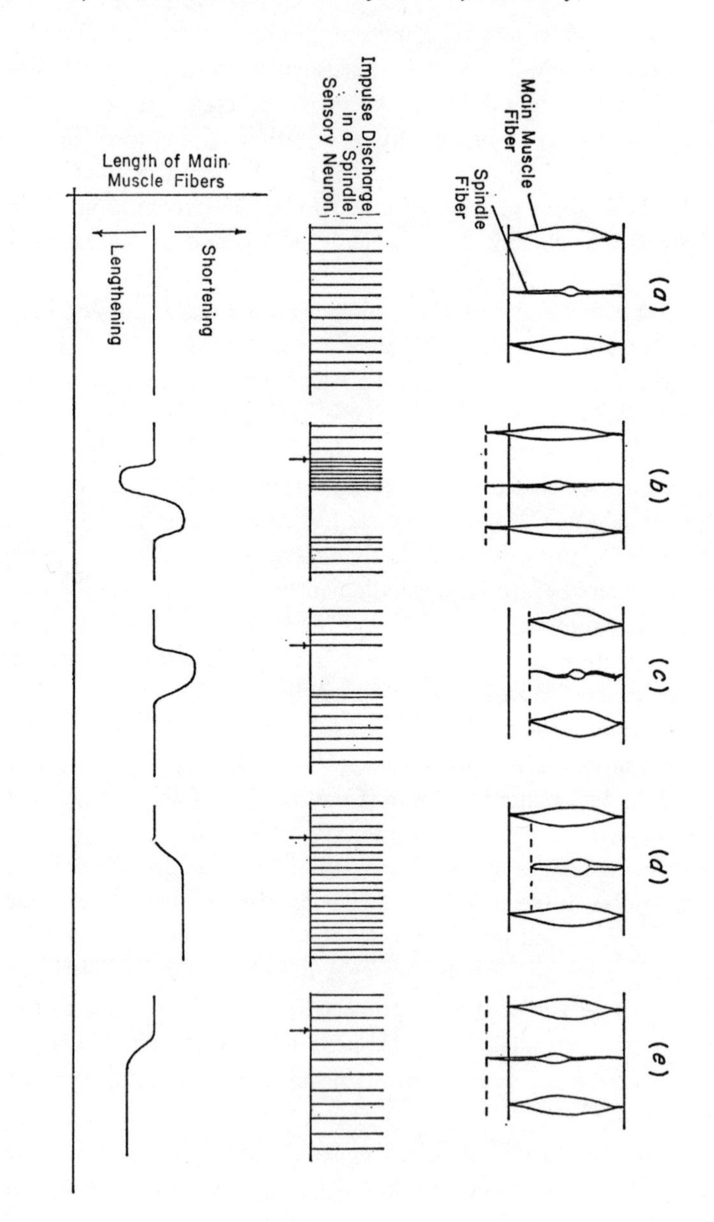

(a)
(b)
(c)
(d)
(e)
Main Muscle Fiber
Spindle Fiber
Impulse Discharge in a Spindle Sensory Neuron
Length of Main Muscle Fibers
Shortening
Lengthening

sible to demonstrate facilitation of synergistic motoneurons and inhibition of antagonistic ones. The flexion reflex (the withdrawal of a limb from a painful stimulus) is more complex. Obviously many synapses and many muscles are involved and the activity of all these muscles is beautifully coordinated. Only one side of the body takes part, however. A further stage in complexity, and closely associated with the flexion reflex, is the crossed extension reflex. If you were paddling in the sea and a crab fastened on to your toes, you would pull your leg up very quickly. Suddenly your other leg has to support the weight of your whole body and, if nothing were done about its muscles, you would fall over. In fact, as you bend one leg, the crossed extension reflex operates. It causes the appropriate muscles to contract and makes your other leg into a firm pillar, which can then support the weight of your whole body. There is no point in multiplying examples. No matter how apparently complicated they may be, all reflexes are made up of the components outlined at the beginning of this chapter. The basic requirements are a system for collecting information and a system for using that information in action.

▶ FIGURE 13–2. The relation between the rate of discharge in a spindle sensory neuron and the length of the main muscle fibers in five different situations. (*a*) The resting muscle showing a permanent background discharge in the sensory neuron. (*b*) The muscle is stretched from outside, putting a strain on the sensory spindle. The rate of impulse discharge increases and causes the main motoneurons to contract and shorten the muscle. This takes the strain off the spindle which ceases to fire impulses. The motoneurons then relax to their resting length and the spindle begins to fire again at the resting level. (*c*) The muscle shortens because of a twitch in the main motoneurons. Tension is taken off the spindle and the sensory neuron ceases to discharge impulses. In turn, this causes the main motoneurons to relax again and the muscle returns to its resting length. (*d*) The small motoneurons fire faster, shortening the spindle muscle fibers. The sensory neurons fire faster; this makes the main motoneurons contract and the muscle shortens to a new level. (*e*) The small motoneurons fire more slowly. The muscle spindles lengthen and the whole muscle follows.

Lastly, we must spend a little time on a rather different type of reflex, the conditioned reflex. The oldest example, used by Pavlov in his original work on the subject, is probably still the best. A dog, and indeed any animal, will produce saliva when it sees food. You have no doubt found this happening to yourself when you have seen a delicious meal waiting for you. Pavlov trained a dog and arranged it so that he could observe the production of saliva. Over a period he gave the dog food at regular intervals and every time when, or just before, the food arrived, a bell was rung, Every time the dog produced saliva. Finally, Pavlov rang the bell without providing the food. Again the dog salivated. Because of the long association of food with the bell, the bell alone eventually became a stimulus which could reflexly excite production of saliva. This type of reaction is called a conditioned reflex.

Much of our own behavior is made up of conditioned reflexes. If you step off the sidewalk and then suddenly hear an automobile horn blaring out, you very quickly leap back. The response is automatic. But you weren't born with it. It was only after much teaching by your parents that you learned that automobiles could be dangerous and that they gave warning by hooting. Only then could the blare of a horn become the stimulus for a conditioned reflex. You can probably think of other examples for yourself. You might care to think about your own behavior and try and estimate how much of it is made up of conditioned reflexes. You may well be surprised at the result.

14 Controlling Our Muscles

We have seen that, even in man, simple reflex activity can be carried out by the spinal cord alone. The movements of a mammal are, however, far too complex to be explained simply on the basis of spinal reflexes. Higher brain centers exert a considerable degree of control. One of the simplest ways of investigating this is to cut the brain at various levels and then to look for any consequences. In 1898, Sir Charles Sherrington first described the condition known as decerebrate rigidity. He sectioned the middle region of a cat's brain, thus cutting off the cerebral cortex and other higher centers from the lower part of the brain and spinal cord. Sherrington observed that after this operation the neck, tail, and all four legs became extremely rigid. The condition was appropriately called decerebrate rigidity. The cut had removed the inhibitory control of the higher centers from the muscles concerned. Instead of being relaxed, they contracted strongly.

The motoneurons supplying these muscles must have been firing at a much faster rate than usual. Motoneurons do not usually discharge spontaneously. They must be fired off by impulses reaching them from elsewhere. Sherrington set out to find the source of the sensory information which was causing the motoneuron to discharge. You may be surprised to learn that this information was coming from the affected muscles themselves.

When the sensory roots of the spinal cord were cut to prevent the impulses reaching the motoneurons, the rigidity vanished. The motoneurons were not being directly excited by higher centers. They were being fired by the discharge of stretch receptors in their own muscles.

Sherrington set the stage for the investigation of the problem by modern techniques. His work clearly showed that the main motoneurons of a muscle were firing at a faster rate because of sensory impulses from the muscle spindles of their own muscle. But how were the muscle spindles being stimulated? We have seen that, normally, contraction of the main muscle takes the strain off the muscle spindles and reduces their rate of discharge. There was the possibility that the muscle spindles were behaving abnormally, or that other stretch receptors were involved, but this was shown not to be the case. When a further twitch was produced in the contracted muscle, the discharge in the sensory roots slowed down as usual.

In Chapter 6, we saw that there were two ways of stimulating a muscle spindle. The main muscle could be stretched from outside, or the small motoneurons could cause the muscle fibers of the spindle itself to contract. In both cases, the spindle would become relatively shorter than the main muscle fibers (see Figure 13–2). Obviously, in decerebrate rigidity, the muscle is not being stretched. It is in a strongly contracted state and much shorter than usual. Nor are the main motoneurons themselves being fired at a faster rate by some other source. As soon as the information coming from their own spindles is cut out by sectioning the sensory roots, their rate of discharge falls to a low level. Could it then be the small motoneurons that are involved? If they were firing at a faster rate, the muscle fibers of the spindles would contract. The sensory neurons in turn would fire faster and cause the main muscle to contract and shorten. The possibility could be tested only by recording the small motoneuron activity.

Suppose then that we set up an experiment in which we record the activity of the small motoneurons. First of all, we measure the rate of discharge in the normal animal. Then we cut across the middle of the brain, producing decerebrate rigidity. If we now look at our record, we shall find that the discharge rate of the small motoneurons has greatly increased. It begins to look as though muscular contraction is normally initiated by the small motoneurons. Their firing causes the muscle spindle sensory neurons also to fire at a faster rate. Lastly, the main motoneurons discharge, the main muscle fibers contract, and the muscle is shortened.

So far we have only discussed the small motoneurons in decerebrate rigidity. This is a rather abnormal situation. Before the idea about their role in initiating muscular contraction can be accepted, we must investigate some more normal cases. When the ear of an animal is twisted, the leg muscles contract. The sequence of events in this reflex has been carefully investigated by recording the activity in both large and small motoneurons and in muscle spindle sensory neurons. In all three types of nerve fiber, activity increases. The crucial point is the timing of the onset of this activity. Almost always it is found that the small motoneurons discharge first, immediately followed by the spindle sensory neurons. Finally, the main motoneuron discharge rate increases, and the muscle contracts.

To make the story completely convincing, we shall just discuss one more experiment. If the neck of a cat is pushed downward, the front legs bend and the back legs become straight. It is as though the animal were bending down to look into a mousehole. We could set up an experiment in which the tension of one of the contracting muscles and the spindle discharge from that muscle are recorded. Suppose we do this. If we push the cat's head down, the rate of spindle discharge will increase, showing that the small motoneurons are firing. The muscle will contract. Now we section the sensory roots of the cord which are carrying impulses from that muscle, and we repeat the experiment. The muscle spindles still fire at a faster rate, and therefore the small motoneurons must be causing the spindle fibers to contract. This time, however, there is no contraction of the muscle. The impulses in the sensory neurons cannot reach the main montoneurons. Thus it seems that, in this reflex also, the instructions for muscular contraction are not given directly to the main motoneurons. They are given first to the small ones. The spindle fibers contract, the sensory neurons fire, and only then are the main motoneurons activated.

The rate of small motoneuron discharge, and therefore the state of contraction of the muscles, can be altered by a large number of higher brain centers. Sometimes the rate is reduced, sometimes increased. Decerebrate rigidity shows that normally the highest part of the brain must exert an inhibitory action. When this restraining influence is removed, the discharge rate increases enormously. Many parts of the brain have been electrically stimulated in order to test their influence on the small motoneurons. The effects of stimulation of the cerebellum and the reticular formation are particularly striking. Some areas produced inhibition of small motoneuron discharge, others excitation. Professor Ragnar Granit was able to record from one spindle neuron which was inhibited by stimulating one point in the reticular formation and excited by another. It is clear that the higher centers exert considerable control over muscular activity. As you can no doubt imagine, the unraveling of the parts which these regions play in coordinating action is going to be a formidable task.

One indication of the complexity of the system appeared when a new method of decerebration was tried. It was pointed out that by trying certain arteries, the blood supply to the upper part of the brain would be cut off. The areas put out of action in this way would be almost identical to those cut off by a knife cut in the middle region of the brain. The only difference with the new method would be that the front part of the cerebellum would also be knocked out. The operation was performed, and sure enough the animal's legs became rigid. The sensory roots of the spinal cord were cut in the expectation that the rigidity would disappear. But it didn't. Obviously, this time the small motoneurons and muscle spindles could not be the cause.

Since the knocking out of the front part of the cerebellum was the only difference between the two operations, it seemed that that region of the brain must be involved. The idea was very neatly confirmed. The midbrain of a cat was cut in the usual way. Rigidity developed, and was abolished by cutting the sensory roots. The front part of the cerebellum was then cooled, putting it out of action; the rigidity returned. When the front part of the cerebellum was warmed again, the rigidity vanished. The conclusion is clear. As in the case of the ordinary rigidity, the source of sensory information was looked for. Various sensory nerves were cooled in order to prevent their impulses from reaching the brain. Nothing happened until the auditory nerves were tried. When they were cooled, the rigidity more or less vanished. When they were warmed again, the rigidity returned. The impulses were coming from the labyrinth, which is such an important sensory organ for enabling an animal to stand upright. Normally, the effect of these impulses on the main motoneurons was controlled by the cerebellum. When the front part of the cerebellum was put out of action, the control was removed and the main motoneurons discharged.

The situation is certainly complicated. Normally, as we have seen, movements seem to be initiated by the small motoneurons. Occasionally, perhaps especially when very sudden movements are vital and the delay in initiating a movement in this way would be dangerous, the main motoneurons are probably fired directly. The cerebellum seems in some way to be concerned in balancing and integrating the activity of the two types of motoneuron. Just how it does this is not known. Yet again we are at the frontiers of knowledge. Continually having to say that we do not know is sometimes very frustrating. But it is also very challenging, and that is what makes the study of neurophysiology so exciting.

Before we close this chapter, we must just take another look at the cerebellum. It is the part of the brain which is most concerned in the coordination of muscular activity. If the cerebellum is removed from a dog, for some time after the operation the animal is completely unable to walk. Its legs seem weak and totally incapable of coordinated movements. You might imagine that it would be very cruel to put a dog in this state in a tank of water, since it would immediately drown. But if you did think this, you would be wrong. A dog which has had its cerebellum recently removed cannot walk, but it can swim. It does not swim very well, and its movements are not very smooth, but it can keep afloat. Why should it be able to do so much better in the water than on dry ground? In the water it does not have to contend with gravity; its body is supported by the surrounding liquid. One of the most important functions of the cerebellum is to enable us to walk, run, jump, sit upright, ride a bicycle, and do a host of other things, while all the time this force of gravity is trying to pull us down toward the earth. The cerebellum is continually adjusting the tension in our muscles to prevent us from falling over. The muscles it uses in this way are almost always the ones which straighten out our legs and enable them to take the strain. The muscles which bend our legs do not have nearly such a difficult task. They have to lift up only the weight of the leg itself; the ones which straighten our legs have to support the whole body. The difference between the two sets of muscles can be very clearly seen if you look at your leg below the knee. Behind there is a great mass of muscle used for keeping the ankle joint firm, and for rising up on your toes when you are walking, running, or jumping. In front, for bending your ankle joint, you have a much smaller mass of muscle which does not have anything like so much to do. Without a cerebellum our muscles would be completely unable to keep us upright. It is the master controller which enables us to move about without falling over under the influence of gravity.

15 The Final Link

So far we have discussed the way information is gathered and we have learned a little about the processes which go on in the central nervous system. We have studied the ways in which motoneurons are caused to discharge impulses and now, in this last chapter to deal only with the nervous system, we shall see how these impulses produce a contraction of the muscle.

As a large motoneuron enters a muscle it splits up into a number of branches. Each of these branches goes to one muscle fiber. This means that a single motoneuron supplies a number of muscle fibers. How many depends on the type of the muscle. In very delicate muscles, like those of the eye, where fine movements must be carried out, each motoneuron may supply only five or six muscle fibers; in some of the leg muscles where coarse, powerful movements are required, two hundred or more muscle fibers may be supplied by one motoneuron.

For our purposes, we can look on a muscle fiber as consisting of three main parts. First of all, there is the end plate, the region where the end of the motoneuron is applied to the muscle fiber membrane. It is really a rather specialized form of synapse. Then there is the rest of the membrane of the muscle fiber. This behaves like an unmyelinated axon in that it conducts all-or-nothing impulses over its surface. These impulses are very similar to ordinary nerve impulses and like them are produced by a sudden

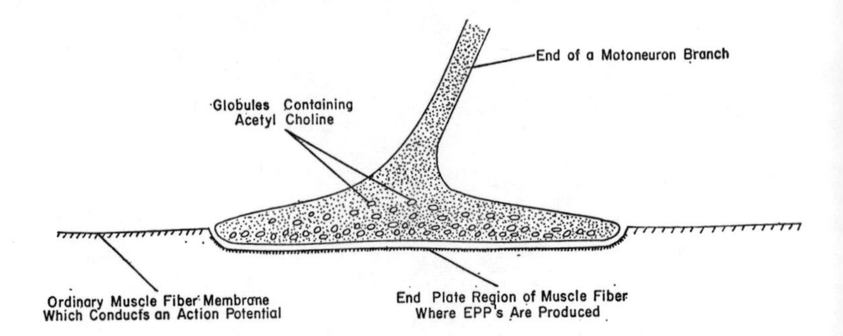

▶ FIGURE 15–1. Simplified diagram of the neuromuscular junction.

increase in sodium permeability. Finally, enclosed in the membrane is the contractile mechanism itself. It is set into operation when an impulse passes over the surface.

As between two neurons, there is a definite gap at the end plate between the motoneuron ending and the muscle fiber. As with ordinary synapses, there is a definite delay before an impulse in the motoneuron fires off an impulse in the muscle fiber. Once again the activity crosses the gap not by electrical, but by chemical, means. Electron microscope studies have shown that in the motoneuron ending there are many tiny vesicles. It is widely assumed that these contain the chemical transmitter which activates the muscle fiber. A large number of the vesicles are probably released whenever a nerve impulse comes along. The neuromuscular junction is the only region where the nature of the transmitter is known with absolute certainty. It is called acetylcholine.

We must now make two journeys; one to South America and one to West Africa. Imagine a South American Indian stalking game in the Amazon jungle. He comes to a clearing in the forest and there, on the other side, catches sight of a deer. Very quietly he draws out an arrow from his quiver, dips the tip in the pot of poison he is carrying, fits it on to his bow, and fires. The deer is hit, but not in a vital part, and bounds away. But very quickly its graceful movements become unsteady. It begins to stagger as if drunk and soon falls to the ground, its muscles paralyzed. It may die because it is unable to breathe, before the hunter can come up and cut its throat. Leaving the Amazon, we shall now make a quick flight over to a West African village where a strange ceremony is taking place. One of the villagers has been losing cattle because of some dangerous disease. Last week his eldest son died. He believes that someone is putting a spell on him and he has accused the grandmother of a rival family of being a witch. She has to submit to trial, not by judge and jury, but by eating a type of bean which grows in the forest. She stands before the assembled village and is forced to eat the beans. The villagers watch breathless with anticipation. The bean begins to have its effect. The old woman sways and faints, her muscles contract violently, her heart stops, and she dies. The villagers look at one another. She was a witch after all. If she had been innocent she would have recovered from the ordeal. It may seem strange, but the arrow poison and the bean have contributed a great deal to our understanding of the way in which activity crosses the neuromuscular junction. Combined with the very modern technique of recording electrical changes at the end plate, they have played a vital role in unraveling the problem.

THE END PLATE POTENTIAL

With a microelectrode in a muscle fiber near the end plate we can pick up the potentials which follow stimulation of the muscle nerve. The record looks similar to the record obtained from inside a motoneuron when an impulse is fired off there. The muscle fiber contracts and, to our annoyance, probably displaces our microelectrode. If we now inject a small dose of curare (the South American arrow poison) into the blood supply of that muscle, we shall see a very different picture when we give a shock to the motoneuron. No impulse will be produced in the muscle fiber. Instead, we shall see a potential change rather like the EPSP of a motoneuron. The muscle fiber does not contract and our microelectrode remains in position. The potential change is not propagated over the surface of the muscle fiber; and if two shocks are given to the motoneuron one after the other, the second potential change will be added to the first. Appropriately enough, this electrical activity is called the end plate potential or EPP. If we increase the dose of curare and repeat the experiment, the EPP will become smaller. If we allow the effect of the curare to wear off, the EPP will gradually become larger. Eventually it will reach the threshold of the muscle fiber membrane and a conducted impulse will be fired off. The EPP results from the change in ionic permeability at the end plate, caused by the acetylcholine release. The change is an increase in permeability to all ions, tending to make the membrane potential zero. For the third time we see the excitatory pattern repeated. In the muscle fiber, as in the ending of a sensory neuron, and as in a motoneuron, there are two types of membrane. At the end plate a graded, nonconducted potential change is produced, which tends to reduce the membrane potential near the end plate to zero. If the drop in potential is large enough, the adjacent second type of membrane is reduced to its threshold potential and a conducted all-or-nothing impulse is fired off.

ACETYLCHOLINE

As we have noted, an impulse in the motoneuron causes acetylcholine to be released. The acetylcholine then quickly diffuses across the gap to the end plate. On the end plate, there are points into which the acetylcholine molecules can fit. Once the acetylcholine molecules are attached to the end plate they produce an increase in the permeability to all ions. It is rather like a lock and key mechanism. The acetylcholine molecule is the key and fits into the keyhole, its point of attachment on the end plate. The molecule is just the right shape to operate the lock, the door is opened and ions can rush in and out. Now what happens when we inject curare? The curare molecule is of a shape which can fit into the keyhole but can not turn the lock. It jams the mechanism, just as you would jam a lock if you tried to operate it with a key which was nearly, but not quite, the right shape. The curare molecules jam up the keyholes on the end plate, so that the acetylcholine molecules cannot attach themselves when they are released from the motoneuron ending. A few may be able to fit in and thus produce a small end plate potential which is quite unable to produce an impulse in the muscle fiber. The latter therefore does not contract and the muscle is paralyzed. It is interesting to note that nowadays curare and certain similar synthetic drugs are used by surgeons. They produce a complete relaxation of the muscles and so make the surgeon's task much easier.

Turning away from curare for the moment, let us think again about what happens at a normal neuromuscular junction. Acetylcholine is released and attaches itself to the end plate. If it stayed there a continuous end plate potential would be produced, a long train of impulses would be fired off, and the contractile mechanism would go into spasm. This clearly does not happen under normal circumstances. The end plate potential rises to a peak and quickly fades away. Only one impulse is produced in the muscle fiber for each impulse that reaches the motoneuron ending. In some way the acetylcholine must be removed from the end plate. In fact, there is a substance at the end plate called cholinesterase which is so designed that it can break the acetylcholine molecule in two. As soon as the acetylcholine has produced its effect it is destroyed by the cholinesterase. Curare is such an effective paralyzing mechanism because not only does it jam the lock, but it cannot be broken up by the cholinesterase. You may remember that one of the effects of the West African bean was that it produced strong contractions of the muscles. We should expect this to happen if the acetylcholine were being released, but not being destroyed. This is in fact the case. The bean contains eserine, a substance which jams the cholinesterase mechanism and prevents it breaking up the acetylcholine. Thus one motoneuron impulse results in a series of impulses in the muscle fiber because the acetylcholine is not destroyed. The muscle then contracts violently. Eserine thus has the opposite effect to curare on the end plate potentials, increasing them in size instead of reducing them. You may be interested to know that if minute quantities of acetylcholine, curare, or eserine are injected inside the muscle fiber, so that they reach the inside of the end plate, they have no effect whatsoever. The keyholes are only to be found on the outside of the end plate. These substances can only produce their effects there.

When we were discussing synaptic transmission in motoneurons, we saw that the motoneuron could be inhibited. This inhibition was brought about by increasing the permeability to potassium and chloride ions so that the membrane potential was increased away from the threshold value. If you have been thinking about inhibition, it may have occurred to you that there is another way in which it could be produced. This is by reducing the amount of excitatory transmitter released by an impulse from the nerve endings. A small amount of chemical could only produce a small potential change which would be insufficient to fire off an impulse in the next cell.

This type of inhibition is known to occur and it has been most clearly described in muscle tissue. In mammalian muscle the only neuron which reaches the end plate is an excitatory one. There is no question in normal circumstances of inhibition taking place at the neuromuscular junction. But in the crayfish the situation is different. At each end plate there are two neurons, one excitatory and one inhibitory. When an impulse passes down the inhibitory neuron, as usual it releases a chemical at the end plate. This inhibitory chemical has two effects. It acts on the muscle end plate to prevent the membrane potential approaching the threshold value. This is similar to the method of inhibition we have already described in motoneurons. However, it also has an effect on the excitatory neuron. If an inhibitory impulse just precedes an excitatory one, the amount of excitatory chemical released is greatly reduced. It has, therefore, much less chance of producing an end plate potential large enough to fire off the muscle fiber. In this case the inhibitory chemical affects both sides of the synapse. It alters the ionic permeability of the end plate to prevent the membrane potential being reduced to the threshold value. In addition, it decreases the amount of chemical released by an excitatory impulse. Its inhibitory action is doubly effective.

It has recently been shown that this type of presynaptic inhibition, as it is called, occurs in mammals as well. It is not found, of course, at the mammalian neuromuscular junction since there is no inhibitory neuron. It does occur at synapses in the central nervous system, increasing the possibilities for complex interaction between neurons. The poor neurophysiologist is constantly uncovering new facts which make his studies more and more intricate and difficult.

THE CONTRACTILE MECHANISM

Finally we shall turn our attention to the actual contractile mechanism of the muscle. Unfortunately this is not yet very well understood. If you were to look at, say, a suitably prepared cat's leg muscle fiber, under a microscope, you would see that all along it there are evenly spaced dark and light transverse striations, while passing along the length of the fiber are faint fibrils. It used to be thought that contraction was brought about by these fine fibrils coiling up like a spring, but this is now known not to be the case. When a muscle fiber does contract, the light striations shorten but the dark ones remain the same length.

In recent years, the problem of muscle structure has been unraveled with the aid of the electron microscope. A muscle fiber is largely made up of two types of protein—actin and myosin. These are arranged in the form of thick, dark myosin filaments, interlocking with the fine, pale actin filaments, as shown in Figure 15–2. The dark bands are produced by the myosin. When the muscle contracts, these filaments do not coil up like springs, as used to be thought. Instead, the thin actin filaments slide in be-

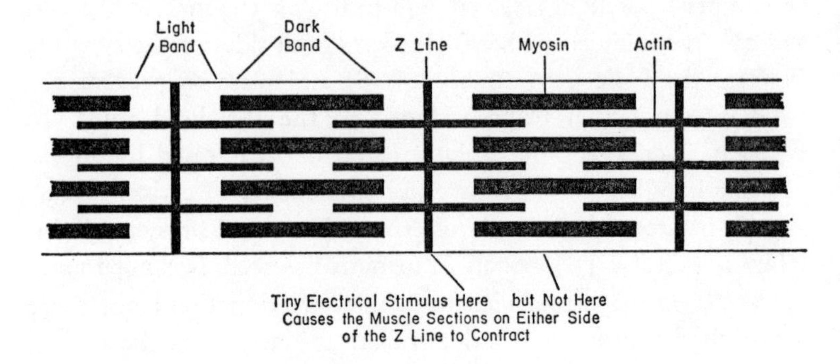

▶ FIGURE 15–2. Schematic diagram showing the structure of a striated muscle fiber.

tween the thick myosin filaments, producing a shortening of the fiber. If you study the diagram in Figure 15–2 you will see that when this happens the dark bands will still remain the same length while the light bands will shorten.

The precise way in which this sliding in and out occurs is still being studied. Similarly, very little is known about the mechanism whereby the passage of an impulse over the surface of a muscle fiber sets off the contraction mechanism. Careful study has shown that in the middle of the light striation there is a fine dark line known as the Z line. This may be a membrane which passes right across the muscle fiber. It has been suggested that this Z structure is involved in passing the excitation from the surface membrane to the interior of the muscle fiber. If a tiny microelectrode is applied to the surface of a muscle fiber at a Z line and the region stimulated by a very small current, the pieces of muscle fiber on either side of that Z line, but nowhere else, contract. If the microelectrode is placed on the muscle fiber away from the Z line a similar stimulus produces no response. This seems to support the idea that the Z line is involved in setting off the contractile mechanism, but a great deal more work must be done if the idea is to become firmly established.

The distinction between the activation of contraction and the contraction itself is not always clearly understood. The trigger which sets the contraction mechanism off seems to be the impulse passing over the surface of the muscle fiber. As we have seen this impulse has all the characteristics of a nerve impulse in an axon. It is of a constant size and its passage leaves the membrane momentarily inactive. This means that two of the impulses can never merge with each other and summate. Each impulse is always distinct and separate from the ones before and after it. The contractile mechanism is very different. Under constant conditions its response to a single isolated impulse is always the same. The single impulse gives a stimulus of constant size and the response is also constant. If we measure the time course of the two processes, however, we shall find that they are very different. The impulse is very quickly over and the membrane will be excitable again, probably within less than a millisecond. Although the impulses cannot summate they can follow each other very rapidly indeed.

The contractile mechanism is very much slower. After a contraction a muscle fiber may take something in the region of a 100 milliseconds to return to its original length. Clearly the muscle fiber membrane could have conducted a large number of impulses in this time. In addition, two contractions following one on top of the other will summate. The contractile mechanism does not have any refractory period. Thus if impulses in the motoneuron follow one another at a time interval of greater than about 100 milliseconds the twitches of the muscle fiber will be clearly separated. If the impulses are separated by less than this, one contraction will be added to the previous one and the muscle fiber twitches will tend to merge. Now, a single twitch not only takes about 100 milliseconds to die away, but may take 20 to 30 milliseconds to reach its peak. If the impulses follow one another at shorter intervals than this, a second impulse will pass over the fiber while the contraction produced by the previous one is still rising. Under these conditions there will be no time for the contractile mechanism to relax at all between two impulses. A smooth steady contraction known as tetanus results. Tetanus usually results in ordinary muscle fibers when impulses reach them at rates of about 50 or more per second.

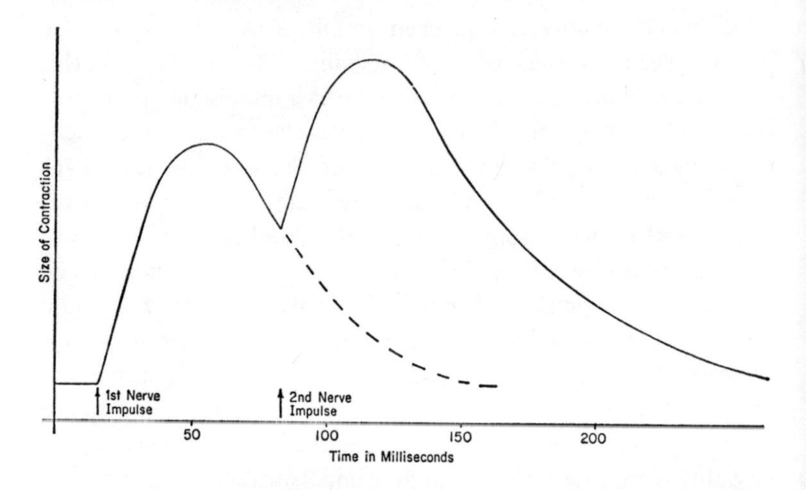

▶ FIGURE 15–3. Summation of two contractions in a muscle. The first nervous impulse arrives at the muscle and fires off a contraction. A second impulse arrives before the muscle has returned to its resting level. This also fires off a contraction which is added on to the first.

In discussing the ways in which information is utilized we have spent most of our time on the striated muscle which makes up the bulk of muscular tissue in a mammalian body. We have done this because much more is known about this than about almost any other type of activity. There are other sorts of muscle. That which is found in our digestive tracts and in our bladders and in a host of other places differs from the muscle we have described in not having striations. Heart muscle is also different; it does not need a nervous impulse to set its contractile mechanism in action, but its rate of beating is controlled by nervous activity. Glands are also often under the control of the nervous system and are stimulated to secrete by nervous impulses. In all these ways, the information collected by the sensory system is used to adjust the activity of the body to the needs of the moment. Much is not understood, much remains to be discovered. There is a wide open field for anyone who has the ability and the inclination to be a neurophysiologist.

16 The Brain and the Pituitary

To look at the pituitary gland, about the size of a pea and firmly embedded in the skull at the base of the brain, you would never dream that it is one of the most important pieces of tissue in the whole body. The early anatomists had great difficulty in suggesting a function for this tiny gland. Some thought that it might be one of the sources of the mucus in our noses and that waste products from the brain were passed out of the body by this route. If you were to read any of those old medical books, you would find that none of their authors really had much idea as to what the pituitary gland was doing. In fact, it was not until the late nineteenth century that the first real clues came to light. People suffering from a whole host of strange diseases were found, after death, to have some abnormality of the gland. Giants and dwarfs, people with strange sexual disorders, highly excitable people, and dull, imbecilic ones all had pituitary disturbances. Perhaps this tiny gland is more important than it appears to be.

Before we can talk about what it does, we must know a little about its anatomy. Basically there are two parts to the gland, one in front, the anterior lobe, and one behind, the posterior lobe. In themselves these two lobes are very interesting because they arise from quite different structures in the embryo. In very early life, long before birth, a little growth passes upward from the roof of the mouth. At the same time, another growth pushes downward from the part of the brain known as the hypothalamus. As the embryo grows, the two meet and fuse together. The connection with the mouth is lost, the one with the brain remains, and the pituitary gland is formed. The front part, the anterior lobe, is very similar in structure to other endocrine glands: it has a rich blood supply to carry away the hormones, but only a very scanty nerve supply. As you might expect, the posterior lobe looks quite different. It is really a continuation of the part of the pituitary known as the median eminence which is embedded in the base of

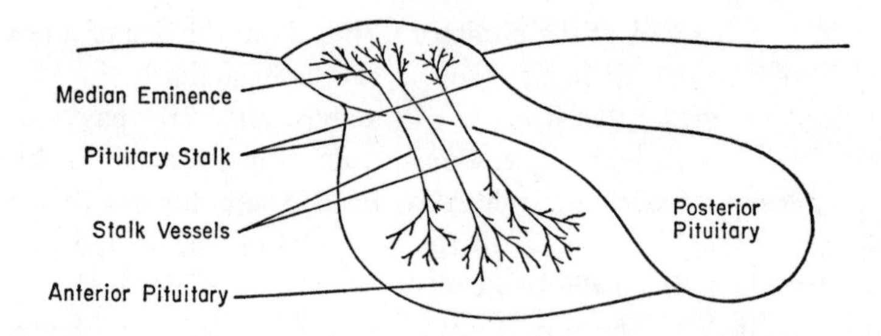

▶ FIGURE 16–1. Outline of the structure of the pituitary.

the brain. Many neurons which have their cell bodies in the hypothalamus have axons which do not synapse with other neurons or with any effector structures. Some of these unusual axons end instead in the median eminence, while others pass down the pituitary stalk to end in the posterior lobe. These parts of the pituitary look much more like the central nervous system than an endocrine gland.

BLOOD SUPPLY

The arrangement of the blood vessels in the pituitary is very important. Both parts of the gland receive an ordinary arterial supply and have an ordinary venous drainage. There is in addition, however, a most peculiar arrangement of blood vessels that has interested research workers for many years. The median eminence, like all other parts of the body, is supplied with blood from an artery. Like ordinary arteries this one divides into smaller and smaller vessels. Eventually it breaks up into a mass of tiny tubes, known as capillaries, which branch and wrap themselves around the neurons. Again, as in ordinary blood systems, these capillaries then come together into larger and larger vessels like veins, which drain the blood away. But unlike normal veins, the blood in these vessels does not go straight back to the heart. It is carried down the pituitary stalk to the anterior lobe of the gland. There the vessels break up again into another mass of capillaries which surrounds the gland cells. Only after this does the blood flow into ordinary veins and then back to the heart. These pituitary stalk vessels are very unusual in that they link two lots of capillaries, one in the median eminence and one in the anterior pituitary. Twice the blood comes into close contact with cells.

It was soon suggested that these pituitary stalk vessels were probably carrying substances from the median eminence to the anterior pituitary. Then the arguments began and many people claimed that the vessels were doing the reverse and carrying material from the anterior pituitary to the median eminence. It is extremely difficult to follow blood vessels in dead animals; and to decide, just by looking carefully at dead preparations of pituitaries, which way the blood is flowing is almost impossible. Nevertheless they tried, and for a long time people argued, giving lots of theoretical reasons why the blood should be flowing in one direction or the other. Of course this was ridiculous and could never give a certain answer. The only way to settle the point was to watch the blood flowing along the pituitary stalk of a live animal. If you have ever looked at an animal's skull and seen just where the pituitary lies, you will perhaps understand why physiologists preferred to talk rather than to do the experiment. If you wanted to devise a more inaccessible place in the body to put a gland, I do not think you could ever find one. It is right in the middle of the head almost completely surrounded by bone. However, at last several physiologists had the courage to try. After many difficulties had been solved they were able to operate on an animal and to look at its pituitary stalk while it was still alive. They obtained the answer without any doubt at all. The blood flowed downward from the median eminence to the anterior pituitary. If the vessels are carrying material between these two regions, they must be carrying it in this direction and not in the other.

WAYS OF INVESTIGATING THE GLAND'S FUNCTION

We now know enough about the structure of the gland to start learning about how it works. In studying glands which produce hormones one of the oldest techniques is to remove the gland from the animal and see what happens when it is deprived of the hormone. Because of the difficulty of getting at the pituitary, it was some time before anyone devised an operation by which the pituitary could be removed without killing the animal. Until this was done, very little progress was made. It had long been suspected that the pituitary was much more complicated than ordinary endocrine glands like the thyroid. As soon as this rather difficult operation for removing the gland was devised, this idea was confirmed. Animals without pituitaries are very strange creatures indeed.

One of the most striking results is that the thyroid gland, the adrenal cortex, and the ovaries (in the female) or the testes (in the male) all decay and cease to work effectively. The animal without a pituitary therefore reacts as though the thyroid, the adrenals, and the sex glands had been removed as well. There are so many things wrong with the creature that it is impossible to unravel all their causes. One of the disturbances is most striking in young animals. Without pituitaries, they stop growing, remain much smaller than their normal brothers and sisters, and soon die. All we can really learn from removing the whole gland is that we are dealing with a very complicated structure which seems to be essential for the proper working of other endocrine glands. We can confirm this by giving an animal without a pituitary injections of ground-up pituitary tissue. If the gland has not been missing for too long, the thyroid, adrenals, and sex glands soon recover. While it is by no means normal, since crude injections can never reproduce the delicate control of hormone levels in a normal creature, such an animal can survive in reasonable health. It certainly gets on much better than an animal which has just had its pituitary removed.

Another technique used in endocrinology is an extension of this first type of experiment. A gland, say a thyroid, may be removed and the animal left for a few days until it develops the typical disorders. If we then transplanted into that animal a thyroid from another animal, provided that the transplant had a good blood supply and remained healthy, the animal would soon become normal again. This can be done with many endocrine glands, and normally it doesn't matter much where the transplant is put, provided that it acquires a good blood supply. The blood is essential for carrying the hormones away. The thyroid may be transplanted to the leg, the arm, or into many other places, and it will work quite happily. It is rather like a workman who, provided he is supplied with good food and pay, does not mind working in any part of the country. Given the condition of a good blood supply, the thyroid can work satisfactorily almost anywhere in the body. Most other endocrine glands are similar to the thyroid in this respect.

Of course physiologists tried to apply this technique to the pituitary. Because of its almost inaccessible position, there was every reason for putting a transplant in some easily approachable part of the body, instead of putting it right back in the middle of the skull. Transplants were made into muscles, bones, the surface of the brain, and a host of other places. None of them seemed to be successful. None could even begin to imitate the action of a real pituitary in a normal animal. At first it was thought that because the gland was so small and easily damaged, the transplants were not getting a proper blood supply. This was certainly true in some of the earlier work, but as techniques improved, transplants were made which had beautifully rich blood supplies; they still did not work. The thyroid, adrenals, and sex glands still atrophied and remained nonfunctional. It was easy to see why the posterior part of the gland would not work under these conditions. It had a rich nerve supply, and this could not be imitated by a transplant, no matter how healthy, in any other part of the body. But most of the hormones were found in extracts of the front part of the gland. This had hardly any nerve supply at all, and there seemed no reason why it should not work.

The results after removing an animal's pituitary and then putting a pituitary back in the same place underneath the hypothalamus were completely different. Provided that the animal was not damaged too much by the complicated operation, it recovered completely and lived a life almost indistinguishable from a normal creature. The transplant obviously worked and kept the other endocrine glands in good order. The pituitary seems to be like a workman who can only work in his home town. Nowhere else can he find precisely the right conditions. Here is quite a problem. Why should this gland, particularly its anterior part, fail to work when transplanted anywhere in the body apart from its natural position directly beneath the hypothalamus?

The suggestion was soon made that the difference between the pituitary beneath the hypothalamus and one anywhere else in the body is that the first of these is supplied by the peculiar pituitary stalk vessels. A gland with this blood supply, it was thought, would function properly; one without it would fail to work. Some material carried by these vessels from the median eminence was supposed to make the pituitary work. The obvious experiment was not to remove the gland but to cut the stalk. This would leave intact the ordinary arterial supply to the anterior pituitary, but would prevent the blood carried from the median eminence by the stalk vessels from reaching the gland tissue. The results were very inconclusive. Sometimes the animals remained completely normal in every way; sometimes they showed disturbances of pituitary function. When the animals were examined after death, it was found that simply cutting the stalk vessels did not stop them carrying blood to the gland. Within a few hours they began to grow across the gap and within a couple of days the blood flow down the stalk was almost normal. The only way to do the experiment properly was somehow to stop the blood vessels regenerating. This was done quite simply by putting a piece of waxed card or metal foil in the cut. The vessels could not grow through this, although when the animal died, a check still had to be made to make sure that they had not grown around it. In every case when it was certain that no regeneration had taken place, the pituitary failed to work and the animal reacted as though the gland had been completely removed. It still remained in position beneath the hypothalamus, it still remained healthy and had a good arterial blood supply, but without the blood coming down the stalk from the median eminence, the anterior pituitary failed to function. In some way, some material produced by the median eminence must stimulate the gland to action.

CONTROL OF URINE FLOW

You may remember Verney's experiments on urine flow in the dog which we looked at in Chapter 7. There we saw how the brain can act as a sensory receptor in a mechanism which controls urine flow. Then we did not discuss how the information collected by the brain is actually used. In his dogs Verney found that urine flow could be greatly reduced by extracts of the posterior gland. Extracts of the anterior part of the gland were quite without effect. It seemed reasonable to assume that receptors in the brain, probably in the hypothalamus, collected information about the osmotic pressure of the blood. This information was then used to regulate the flow of hormone from the posterior pituitary. The hormone known as ADH (antidiuretic hormone) was emptied out into the blood and carried to the kidney. There it caused water to be reabsorbed from the urine and held back in the body instead of flowing out. This very plausible theory became widely accepted.

One problem was the source of the hormone. Neurons were not known to produce hormones, and the other cells in the posterior pituitary did not look very likely candidates for the post of ADH manufacturers. Then a very strange fact came to light. Not only was ADH found in the posterior lobe itself, it could also be extracted from parts of the hypothalamus. These regions were the ones containing the cell bodies of the axons passing down into the posterior pituitary. The suspicion grew that the old idea about neurons not producing hormones was perhaps not strictly true. In recent years, a great deal of evidence, much of it very technical, has accumulated. It is now believed that ADH, or something which gives rise to ADH, is manufactured in the cell bodies of certain neurons in the hypothalamus. It then passes down the axons of these neurons into the posterior pituitary. The terminals of the axons are very closely surrounded by capillary blood vessels and nothing would be easier than for ADH to pass from the nerve ending into the blood. Very few people would now deny that, at least in general terms, this is what happens.

This is rather exciting. The nervous and endocrine systems are both very important for controlling the activity of the body. For a long time it seemed as though they were completely different and separate. Already, however, we have seen that nerve cells pass messages from one to the other by using chemical transmitters. Here, in ADH, we have a chemical which is made by a nerve cell but is released into the general circulation just like a hormone. It makes much more real the idea of the unity of these two great systems, for here we have a mechanism which is both nervous and hormonal. The two aspects are bound together in the closest possible way. Many workers have shown that a great variety of nervous stimuli, in addition to osmotic pressure, can alter the output of ADH. One of the greatest physiologists who has ever lived, Claude Bernard, noticed, over a hundred years ago, that human beings who were emotionally upset often had a reduced rate of urine secretion. Exercise, too, is well known to slow down the flow of urine. This is probably not so much due to the exercise itself, but to the emotional strain which it produces. Dogs which are excreting urine rapidly show a marked reduction in urine flow when they are forced to exercise on a treadmill. If the experiment is repeated time after time, the response no longer occurs. The exercise itself remains precisely the same as in the first experiment, but the dogs have become used to it and are no longer emotionally disturbed by it. In those experiments when the dogs had become used to the exercise, if a sudden loud noise was made, the urine flow again slowed down. In fact, any unpleasant or exciting stimulus could inhibit the secretion of urine. For a long time this response to stimuli which obviously affected the nervous system primarily was not understood. At last now we can see why nervous stimuli should be able to bring about an endocrine response.

THE ANTERIOR PITUITARY

You are no doubt thinking that while this is all very well for the posterior lobe of the gland, which has such obvious nervous connections, the anterior lobe is a very different kettle of fish. It is in some ways even more interesting than the posterior lobe. Just as Claude Bernard observed that emotional stresses could alter urine flow, so several physiologists noticed that nervous stimuli apparently could alter the activity of the anterior lobe of the pituitary. Everyone knows that many birds and animals have regular breeding seasons which, in the wild state, are associated with the season of the year. Some of the most interesting work has been done on ferrets. These animals usually have a very well-defined breeding season in the spring and early summer. However, if they are kept in a laboratory, their breeding season can be altered by varying the lighting conditions. If female ferrets are in cages where the light remains on for longer periods and is more intense than ordinary daylight, they are ready to breed much sooner than are female ferrets kept in cages which are illuminated naturally. Not surprisingly, the response does not occur in a blind animal. Still not surprisingly, but a little more unexpectedly, it does not occur in an animal without a pituitary. Once again here is a possible link-up between the nervous and endocrine systems.

Even more striking is the release of eggs (ovulation) in many animals. As you know, before an embryo can be formed, an egg from the ovary of the female must unite with a sperm from the testes of the male. In mammals, sperm are deposited in the female genital tract during the act of sexual intercourse. It is obviously no good for an egg to be released from the ovary long before or long after intercourse takes place. The sperm and the egg would then have no chance of meeting and no embryo would be formed. In many mammals (but not in man) intercourse itself sets in motion a train of events which results in one or more eggs being released from the ovaries. This is clearly an excellent arrangement since the egg is released just at the right time, when the sperm are in the female genital tract, and there is an excellent chance of their meeting. This fact has long been known, but the precise way in which it works is only now being investigated in detail. Most experiments have been done on the rabbit.

As far as sensory receptors which set off the mechanism are concerned, a whole host of them are involved. Probably the most important is the physical stimulation of the female genital organs. Seeing, smelling, or hearing a male can also help to set off ovulation. All these stimuli probably have a similar effect, the production of a state of high sexual excitement. Ovulation still occurs even if all nervous connections to the ovary have been severed and if the ovary has been transplanted to another site in the body. The final stimulus must therefore be carried by the blood and is almost certainly hormonal. Once again we have a situation where nervous stimuli produce an endocrine response. Once again the two systems are united in a single mechanism.

We are fortunate in that, in recent years, much has been

discovered about the details of the processes involved. Since it was known that the anterior pituitary produces hormones which can control the activity of the ovary, it seemed natural to look in this direction for the link between nerves and hormones. When the rabbit was studied in detail, it was found that eggs were normally released from the ovary about ten hours after sexual intercourse. Professor A. S. Parkes of Cambridge found that if the pituitary gland was removed within one hour after intercourse, ovulation did not take place. If the pituitary was removed any later than this, the eggs were released as usual. From this experiment we can draw the conclusion that within one hour of intercourse, the anterior pituitary has released enough hormone to produce ovulation nine or ten hours later.

In an effort to imitate the effects of intercourse, several workers tried stimulating various parts of the nervous system. They hoped in this way to bring about ovulation. As usual, unforeseen difficulties and bad techniques spoiled much of the earlier work. Eventually, however, Professor G. W. Harris used an excellent remote control method of stimulation. Suppose you have two coils of wire, one inside the other. You probably know that, by passing a current through the outer coil, you can cause a current to flow in the inner coil, even if there is no direct connection between the two. Harris, like Verney, used a preliminary operation so, that, during the real experiment, the animal should be disturbed as little as possible. He implanted electrodes with their tips in different parts of rabbits' brains. But these were not ordinary electrodes connected to a battery or to a main supply to bring about electrical stimulation. The top of the electrode, which protruded just above the skull, had wrapped around it a tiny coil consisting of many turns of fine wire. The electrode and the coil were fixed to the skull by means of a special cement. The skin of the rabbit's scalp was sewn over the top of the whole thing, and the animal allowed to recover completely. When an experiment was being carried out, the rabbits were kept in a fairly small cage which had wrapped around its outside a large coil of wire. When the current was passed through this outer coil, a current was also induced in the tiny coil embedded in the rabbit's skull. Current therefore also passed down the electrode, which was insulated except for its very tip. The area of brain around the tip of the electrode was thus stimulated. Animals could be stimulated in this way even when they were unanesthetized and freely moving. The release of eggs by the ovary could then be looked for several hours later. The consensus of the results of experiments by Harris and others is that, while stimulation of various parts of the hypothalamus can produce ovulation, prolonged stimulation of the anterior pituitary itself brings about no response. By far the most sensitive area is in the region of the median eminence, where stimulation for as little as three minutes resulted in full ovulation. As with the gland itself, stimulation of the pituitary stalk had no effect.

These results are particularly interesting for us. They suggest that the sensory information about sexual intercourse is probably coordinated in the hypothalamus. The last stage in the nervous part of the mechanism seems to be in the region of the median eminence, since the lowest levels of stimulation are effective there. The pituitary gland is essential for the response, but neither it nor its stalk can be electrically excited, so presumably nerves are not involved. How then can the nervous stimulus of intercourse cause a release of hormones from the pituitary? It is here that we must come back to that peculiar arrangement of blood vessels which runs along the pituitary stalk from the median eminence to the anterior lobe. Several experiments, you remember, showed that the gland itself cannot work if those vessels are interrupted. Does it not seem to you likely that the neurons of the median eminence release into these vessels chemical substances which pass to the pituitary and cause the hormones to be released? To many this seems the only conclusion that can be drawn, although we must admit that some workers may not agree with it. Once more we are at the frontiers of knowledge. Is there one chemical for all the pituitary hormones, or is there a separate one for each hormone? What is the nature of these substances? Do they act as a fine or a coarse control for the blood levels of pituitary hormones? All these questions remain to be answered. Light will be thrown on some of them in the next two chapters. Others must yet remain completely obscure. Yet, despite all the doubt, we do seem to have hit on something which is neither a nervous transmitter nor a hormone, but something between the two. It is released from nerve cells into the blood. It does not pass into the general circulation but into a very specialized system of blood vessels.

17 Growth, Maturity, and Stress

In the last chapter, we saw the pituitary as a vital link between the nervous and endocrine systems. In Chapter 4, the gland was described as "the foreman of the endocrine factory." Clearly physiologists believe that it is a most important structure, but what exactly does it do? Four of its hormones are concerned with sex and reproduction. They are not essential for the life of any particular individual, but without them no mammal could produce offspring. If some evil spirit decreed that, from today, no human being could produce any of these hormones, the whole human race would die out. The pituitary is vital for the survival of a species and we shall be thinking about this aspect of its functioning in the next chapter. Unlike the sex hormones, some of the pituitary hormones are essential for the life of the individual. They all seem to have very long names which will be stated once here. Afterward, the substances will be called by their initials. The ones we shall be discussing in this chapter are the somatotropic hormone (STH), the thyroid-stimulating hormone (TSH), the adrenocorticotropic hormone (ACTH), and the antidiuretic hormone (ADH). Having got over these tongue-twisting words, we can now turn to studying the actual hormones.

STH

The over-all effect of STH is well illustrated by two of the pathological conditions which first drew attention to the pituitary. Dwarfs result when there is too little STH, giants when there is too much. Obviously, STH somehow controls the size of an animal. It does not, on the other hand, have much effect on the maturity of an animal. Provided that STH is the only hormone which is deficient, a dwarf as he grows up will become fully adult in almost everything except body size. His mental processes and attitudes, and his sexual maturity are not usually affected. This is in complete contrast to the effects of TSH deficiency. When TSH is in short supply, the thyroid fails to function properly and a cretinous person results. Such a person will be smaller than normal, but the size contrast will not be so great as it is in STH deficiency. The thyroid hormone has, however, a marked effect on the development of maturity. Mental processes and attitudes fail to mature as the cretin grows older. He remains an imbecile, and by no stretch of the imagination can he be called an adult. There is, of course, a great deal of overlapping, but in the broadest of terms, STH controls an animal's size, TSH controls its maturity.

A hormone like STH which produces such a startling effect on body size could act in several ways. STH does, in fact, have so many actions that for a long time endocrinologists thought that more than one substance must be involved. To some extent the strands have now been unraveled, and it now seems certain that all the varied effects are brought about by the one hormone, STH. In any vertebrate (animal with a backbone), the basic structure on which all the soft tissues are hung is the skeleton. This must be fundamental in determining an animal's size. You cannot have a large animal with a small skeleton or a small animal with a large skeleton. This is so obvious that the action of STH on bone growth was one of the first things to be studied. Most bones grow in length by adding new bone to two regions, one near each end of the bone. When these regions become inactive, the bone will not grow any more. As an animal grows up, the areas of bone growth become inactive one by one, until by the adult stage they have almost all ceased to work. By now you will probably have guessed what is coming. One of the fundamental actions of STH is to control the bone growth regions. If there is too little STH, bone growth will cease very early in life and both the skeleton and the over-all body size will remain small. If there is too much STH, bone growth will continue long after it has normally ceased and a giant will be the result. Very occasionally, due to a pituitary tumor, large quantities of STH are produced in middle or old age. By this time most of the bone growth regions have become permanently inactive, but a few of them can be restarted. As a result, while some bones, particularly those of the face and hands, start growing again, others do not respond. The skeleton becomes very distorted, and such unfortunate people often have huge jaws and hands, quite out of proportion to the rest of the body.

While the skeleton forms the basis for body size, the bones must be clothed with soft tissues, and STH also controls these. Very broadly speaking, the bulk of our food is made up of three types of substance. These are proteins, fats, and carbohydrates. The proteins are primarily concerned with the actual building up of body tissues. The fats and carbohydrates provide the energy which those body tissues can use. STH alters the way in which the body treats all three types of food material. We cannot go into the details here, but STH increases the rate at which food protein is built up into body protein. It makes fat energy more available to the tissues, and it helps to store up carbohydrate for the body's use. We shall be thinking more about this when we discuss insulin in Chapter 20.

One of the most important jobs that STH does is to help the other pituitary hormones to carry out their own tasks properly. Suppose that we remove the pituitary from an adult animal. Very soon, that animal's thyroid, adrenal cortex, and sex glands will become small and inactive. What will happen to these organs if we inject STH into the animal? Very little; they will remain in much the same condition and be inactive. On the other hand, what would happen if we injected TSH alone into the animal? The thyroid would be partially repaired and would begin to secrete the thyroid hormone. But the gland would not look nearly so healthy as in a normal animal. Lastly, what would happen if we injected both STH and TSH? The result would be dramatic. The thyroid would rapidly become healthy and apparently function completely normally. STH alone has no effect on the gland. TSH alone brings about a partial recovery. The two together restore the thyroid to full health. They work in cooperation with each other. STH has this same action on the adrenals and the sex glands. Alone it has no effect, but when given with ACTH and the pituitary sex hormones, it can bring about a complete recovery of glandular function. It is obviously a very versatile hormone.

ACTH

The adrenal glands lie in the abdomen just above the kidneys. Each is made up of two parts, an outer region known as the cortex, and an inner one known as the medulla. The cortex produces several hormones, known as steroids because of their chemical composition. The main product of the medulla is epinephrine, a quite different chemical compound. In an animal without ACTH, the cortex atrophies and the medulla does not. The medulla seems to be completely different in function and we shall discuss it in Chapter 19. Here we shall be thinking about the cortex.

Many hormones have been found to come from the adrenal cortex. It would be boring and confusing if I were to list them all here. If the adrenal cortices are removed, many different disorders result. At one time it was hoped that each one of these different disorders might be ascribed to lack of a particular steroid hormone. Regrettably that hope has now been dashed. Like STH, all the cortical hormones have a number of actions.

One steroid might be more active in one direction than in another, but it is impossible to put the functions of the hormones into neat compartments. It will probably be best if here we discuss the actions of the adrenal cortical steroids as a whole, and make no attempt to ascribe particular functions to particular hormones. An animal from which the adrenal glands have been removed very quickly dies. Its body functions are upset in many ways, but they can be broadly divided into two groups. On the one hand, the body loses control of the water and the inorganic ion content of the blood and other fluids. On the other, it loses control of the way it treats the organic substances—fat, protein, and carbohydrate.

Any animal is constructed to work with particular concentrations of inorganic ions in its blood and in its cells. It only functions efficiently when the osmotic pressure of the body fluids is kept at a steady level. An animal will also only work properly at one particular blood volume. If there is too much blood, the heart cannot pump it around the vessels and the animal dies of heart failure. If there is too little blood, food materials, waste matter, oxygen, carbon dioxide, heat, hormones, and a host of other things can no longer be carried around the body. Again the animal dies. Both the osmotic pressure and the volume of the body fluids must be adjusted to the correct levels if an animal is to remain healthy. This adjustment cannot take place without the hormones of the adrenal cortex. In their absence, sodium is rapidly lost from the body via the kidneys. Because of the nature of the osmotic pressure relationships between the urine and the blood, it is impossible to lose large quantities of sodium without losing large quantities of water as well. The blood volume falls and the animal dies because of failure of the circulation. Many other changes in the ionic content of the body take place and contribute to the death, but failure of sodium and water to be retained in the blood seems to be the most important factor. The other changes are too complex and too poorly understood for us to spend time in discussing them here. A number of adrenal hormones help in keeping sodium back from the urine, but by far the most important one is called aldosterone. I have broken my rule and singled this one out because, as we shall see later, it seems to be controlled by a mechanism which is different from the one which controls the other cortical hormones.

The other aspect of cortical function is the control of carbohydrate, protein, and fat metabolism. Carbohydrate is the most important of these three as far as supplying an animal's immediate energy needs are concerned. However, in certain conditions both fats and protein can be used to supply energy. Without the cortical hormones, an animal uses up its carbohydrate supplies very rapidly and wastefully. This is bad enough, but it is made worse by the fact that under these conditions carbohydrate does not appear to be properly absorbed from the gut. The final disaster is that the processes whereby protein and fat can be used to supply energy are greatly slowed down. These disorders all lead to the same end. The animal has no readily available source of energy. What would happen if you exposed such a creature to a strain such as putting it in cold surroundings or forcing it to run a long distance? It would simply be unable to cope with the stress and would probably die. This is one of the most important functions of the cortical steroids. They help us to adjust to all the strains and stresses which we encounter in ordinary life.

Like an animal without adrenals, one without a pituitary cannot respond properly to stress. Even though the adrenals may be still intact, they do not seem to be able to help in the absence of the pituitary. Without ACTH, the body cannot control the output of adrenal cortical hormones. Normally ACTH probably works entirely through the adrenal gland. If large amounts of ACTH are injected into an animal without adrenals, they do apparently have some actions in their own right. But in a normal animal, these large concentrations are probably never reached and all the actions of ACTH are due to its stimulation of the outflow of cortical hormones. The only adrenal steroid over which ACTH does not seem to have complete control is aldosterone. It does alter the aldosterone output partially, but it is very likely that another hormone is really the major controlling factor. Interestingly enough, like ADH which is also concerned with governing urine output, the aldosterone control hormone seems to be made by nerve cells in another part of the brain. We still know very little about this and at present, in a book of this sort, nothing more can really be said on the subject.

An increase in blood ACTH causes a rapid increase in the outflow of hormones from the cortex. A decrease in ACTH has the reverse effect. Clearly ACTH controls the cortical steroids, but what controls the ACTH? Oddly enough, it is apparently the cortical hormones themselves. If we remove the adrenals from an animal, there is an enormous increase in the blood level of ACTH. When the cortical hormones are removed from the blood in this way, the pituitary pours out ACTH, in a vain attempt to restore their levels to normal. Suppose, on the other hand, we were to inject large amounts of steroids into a normal animal over a period of time. What would we find if, at the end of this period, we opened up the animal and examined its adrenals? They would have atrophied and shrunk. When the blood level of cortical hormones is raised in this way, the pituitary seems to realize what is happening and decreases its output of ACTH. So long as we continue to inject the hormones, there is no need for the body itself to produce them and so the adrenals become inactive. High levels of blood cortical hormone depress the output of ACTH. Low levels increase it. This sort of relationship which we first discussed in Chapter 4 is known as negative feedback. It is certainly involved in controlling the output of ACTH, TSH, and the pituitary sex hormones. It is absolutely vital for keeping the body running smoothly.

There are three fundamental ways in which the output of any product from any manufacturing process can be controlled. Consider a factory which has one production line (one complete set of machinery) for making cars. Outside the factory, there is a large space in which the finished cars can be kept before being driven away. Suppose the production line is working at a steady rate. How can we alter the rate at which cars leave the factory? By far the simplest method is not to touch the production line at all, but to control the rate at which cars leave the storage space. If the storage space were full to start with, we could allow the cars to leave more quickly. Eventually, however, we would empty the storage space, and we should have to fall back to the rate at which the cars were coming off the production line. On the other hand, we could slow down the rate at which cars left the factory by putting them into the storage space. If the production line kept working steadily, the space would soon become full. When this happened, in order to make room for cars coming off the line, for every car made we should have to drive one away. Once again, cars would be leaving the factory at the same rate at which they were made. Quite obviously, we can alter the car output in this way only within very narrow limits. We can never make it very different for a long period from the rate at which the cars are coming off the production line. In order to produce a more fundamental alteration in rate, we shall have to go to the manufacturing process itself.

Here we could increase the output in two quite different ways. We could increase the supply of raw materials coming into the factory and induce the workmen to work harder. This would alter the rate and increase our upper limit in a much more fundamental way than by simply making the cars leave the storage space more rapidly. Yet it would still be very definitely limited. There is a limit to the rate at which men and machines can work, and no matter how hard we tried, by this means we could not increase the car output any further. There is only one way in which we could escape these limits almost indefinitely, and that is by buying more machinery and setting up more production lines. By doing this, we could vastly increase car output.

So we could control in three ways the rate at which cars left the factory. We could alter the rate at which the finished product leaves storage, we could alter the rate at which the machinery works, and we could alter the actual amount of machinery we possess. Precisely the same thing is true of the body. Hormones, like all other body constituents, are built up by means of special protein molecules called enzymes. Each hormone has a special set of enzymes designed to manufacture that hormone. The enzymes form the machinery which runs the animal body. Suppose that we want to alter the blood level of a hormone. We could do it by changing its rate of release from storage in the gland, by changing the rate at which the enzymes work, or by actually altering the amounts of the enzymes themselves. By making more sets of enzymes we could increase hormone output; by destroying some of the old ones we could decrease it. A few glands, particularly the sex glands and the adrenal cortex, do not seem to be able to store the hormones they produce. In these cases, only the second and third methods of controlling the rate of hormone output are available. The hormones are passed out into the blood as soon as they are made. Other glands, notably the thyroid and the pituitary, can store their hormones. With them, all three methods of controlling the blood level of the hormone are available and they are probably all used.

In the case of the adrenals, ACTH probably causes more enzymes to be manufactured as well as increasing the rate of working of the enzymes that are already in existence. Precisely how the cortical hormones control the flow of ACTH is not known. Evidence has been put forward both for a direct action on the anterior pituitary and also for an action on the median eminence, thus altering the quantity of some chemical flowing down the pituitary stalk vessels. As is usual in such cases, each side tends to deny the other's story. Also, as is usual, they probably both are partly true. There seems no reason why, for instance, the general level of ACTH should not be controlled by the cortical hormones themselves acting directly on the pituitary cells to control the rate of ACTH production. On the other hand, the hour-by-hour, short-term fine control might be better carried out by the nervous system acting through the median eminence and the stalk vessels. There are many possible variations on this theme. When the system is finally worked out, we shall probably find that all three types of control operate and that they work partly by the action of the cortical hormones directly on the gland cells and partly by means of nervous receptors in the hypothalamus. These would measure hour-by-hour fluctuations in the blood levels and, by means of chemical messengers carried down the stalk vessels, adjust the rate of ACTH release. It will be many years, however, before we know the control system in such detail.

TSH

In most mammals, the thyroid consists of two lobes which lie in the throat on either side of the windpipe. TSH is absolutely essential for the proper functioning of this gland. It seems to operate in all the three ways which we discussed in the last section. It controls the quantities of the enzymes which make the thyroid hormone, it controls the rate at which those enzymes work, and it controls the rate at which the hormones are released from storage. The thyroid hormone itself contains iodine. If there is not enough iodine in the diet, the hormone cannot be synthesized. Water in countries, especially mountainous ones, which are far from the sea contains hardly any iodine. The lack of it is the reason why so many cretins used to be found in Switzerland and why they still are found in remote regions of the Himalayas. If there is some iodine in the water, but the amount is still insufficient, a less severe form of thyroid ailment may result. Because of insufficient iodine, the thyroid cannot produce enough hormone, and the blood levels of the latter are low. In an attempt to raise the blood level, the pituitary pours out TSH. This stimulates the thyroid gland to grow, but because of the iodine lack it can never produce enough hormone. The gland grows and grows and in severe cases may cause a swelling as big as a football to appear at the front of the neck. Many years ago, this type of swelling, known as goiter, was very common even in some parts of the United States. Now, fortunately, it is very rare, mainly because tiny quantities of iodine are added to many types of table salt. This is why, when salt is advertised, you may be told that it is iodized. The iodine in it provides part of the raw material for the synthesis of the thyroid hormone.

As with ACTH and the adrenal cortex, the actions of TSH seem to be due entirely to its effect on the thyroid. In experiments, or in disease, when blood levels of TSH are abnormally high, it may act on some tissues in its own right, but the likelihood of this happening in a normal animal is not very great. The main action is undoubtedly to increase the blood level of the thyroid hormone. Again in a similar way to the cortical hormones and ACTH, high levels of thyroid hormone in the blood depress the output of TSH. Also again, there is the quarrel between those who believe that the thyroid hormone acts directly on the pituitary cells and those who believe that it operates via the hypothalamus and the median eminence. Both groups are probably partially right, and both levels of control seem to operate. Very minute amounts of thyroid hormone injected into both the hypothalamus and into the pituitary itself depress TSH output. Whether they operate at the level of TSH synthesis or of TSH release is unknown.

How does the thyroid hormone itself act on the body? At present the answer is only known in general terms. In the section on STH, we saw that, while STH controls body size, TSH, through the thyroid, controls maturity. Human beings whose thyroids do not function do not simply remain physically small. They do not grow up mentally and remain like small children all their lives. This effect on maturity is particularly clear when studies are made on animals like frogs, which show a startling change in body form as they grow up. If the thyroid gland is removed from a tadpole, it will not develop legs, its tail will not disappear, and it will not become a frog. If, on the other hand, normal tadpoles are kept in water which contains thyroid hormone, they will change into frogs much earlier than usual. In neither case is there a very marked immediate effect on physical size. Tadpoles without thyroids continue to grow and become larger than usual, but they can never become frogs. Tadpoles fed on thyroid hormone change into frogs when they are the size of ordinary tadpoles. A thyroidless tadpole may be bigger than a thyroid-fed frog.

The details of the way the thyroid works in other ways are not very well known. What is known, is that no tissue in the body seems to be able to work properly without it. It probably acts in some very fundamental way on the mechanisms of energy supply in all cells. It appears to be essential for helping an animal to adapt to conditions of low temperature. Under these circumstances, the output of thyroid hormone is increased, and, as a result, the body generates more heat. While normal rats can survive low temperature conditions very well, rats whose thyroids have been removed seem incapable of doing this. The changes occur very rapidly. Indications of TSH release have been seen within thirty minutes of exposing a guinea pig to very cold conditions. This is very quick, and it is likely that it is another case of the nervous system cooperating with the endocrine system by means of the pituitary gland.

ADH

With one exception, all the hormones which we have so far discussed in this chapter come from the anterior lobe of the pituitary. That exception is the hormone which may control aldosterone output and which is thought to be synthesized by neurons in another part of the brain. Aldosterone controls urine output, and it is interesting that ADH, another hormone which helps to control the urine flow, is also synthesized by neurons. They carry it down the pituitary stalk and then release it into the blood vessels in the posterior lobe of the gland. We have already said quite a lot about ADH in chapters 7 and 16, and it is beyond the scope of this book to discuss its detailed action on the kidney. In the section on ACTH, we noted that both the volume of the body fluid and its ion content must be controlled if the animal is to remain healthy. Aldosterone attacks the problem primarily from the ionic side and makes the kidneys hold back sodium ions instead of passing them out into the urine. ADH, on the other hand, operates mainly on the water side. It causes water to be held back from the urine. In certain diseases, people suffer from lack of ADH. As a result, vast quantities of urine are secreted every day. In a normal animal, both aldosterone and ADH are essential for adjusting the volume and ionic content of the blood and other fluids.

You are now perhaps beginning to see just why the pituitary is so important. It is not surprising that it has been nicknamed "the foreman," or "the master gland." The next chapter, on reproduction and sex, will show you how important it is for the existence of the species as well as for the life of the individual.

18 Keeping the Species Going

The pituitary gland produces four hormones which are essential for reproduction. Two act primarily on the sex glands, one acts on the breasts and the uterus, one on the breasts alone. All these hormones are present in both males and females, although in the male, quite what the ones which are acting on the breasts and uterus are doing, no one seems to know. The two pituitary hormones which act on the sex glands were originally named because of their effects in the female. They are called follicle-stimulating hormone (FSH) and luteinizing hormone (LH). They are now known to be precisely identical to the hormones which occur in the male, but they are still usually referred to by the old names of LH and FSH, even when the male is under discussion. We shall follow that practice here. If we gave the hormones in the male and female different names, we might tend to forget that they are, in fact, identical.

You may find it difficult to believe that the hormones produced by both male and female pituitaries are the same. A great deal of work has now been done to confirm this, but it can be convincingly shown by a single very clever experiment. Female mammals show cycles of sexual behavior; males do not. If the pituitary gland is removed from a female mammal, the cycles cease and, in effect, the animal becomes sexless. However, if, when the female pituitary is removed, one from a closely related male animal is put in place of it, the female shows no sexual disturbances. The cycles may be interrupted for a short while due to the stress of the operation, but they very soon return. A male pituitary gland can enable a female mammal to live a completely normal sex life. This could hardly be the case if the male and female pituitary hormones differed from each other.

What do FSH and LH do? Very broadly speaking, FSH seems to control the production of the germ cells, the eggs and the sperm. LH controls the output of sex hormones from the testes and the ovaries. The action of LH has been conclusively demonstrated in both sexes. The action of FSH has only been convincingly proved in the female. In the male, FSH certainly has no action on the hormone output from the testis, and it does appear very likely that it is essential for the production of sperm. The testis manufactures only one major hormone, testosterone, although several other compounds have been found in tiny amounts. The most important function of testosterone is to stimulate the growth of the sperm. It also passes out into the blood stream and has very widespread actions. It causes the genital organs to grow and mature, it makes hair grow on the face and on the body, it causes a boy's voice to break, and helps to make his muscles strong. Almost all the physical and mental characteristics with which we associate masculinity are due to testerone. The female ovary synthesizes not one hormone, but two, estradiol and progesterone. Estradiol in its actions very roughly corresponds to testosterone. Under its influence, the genital organs grow, the skin is kept soft and smooth, and the breasts develop as the girl becomes a woman. (Some other compounds made by the body, and some which are artificially made, have similar actions to those of estradiol. All compounds that have these effects may be called by the general name of estrogen.) Progesterone is more concerned with the formation and growth of an embryo than with the sexual development of the female. It is probably essential for the release of the egg from the ovary, and it is certainly vital right through pregnancy until the baby is born.

The way in which the blood levels in the female of both pituitary and ovarian hormones are controlled is one of the most difficult problems in the whole of endocrinology. In the male the problem is apparently much simpler, although even there there are more question marks than answers. What is certain is that in man, and in most male mammals, there is no marked sexual cycle. The output of sperm and testosterone seems to remain at a fairly steady level. This implies that FSH and LH also remain at a steady level. The nicest hypothesis would be that testosterone inhibits both FSH and LH when its blood concentration rises above a certain level. When it falls below that level, the output of pituitary hormone increases to bring the testosterone level up again. However, while no one has disproved this, no one has proved it either. One of the chief difficulties is that, at the moment, we cannot accurately and easily measure the concentrations of FSH, LH, and testosterone in the blood. Most assay methods rely on observing the effects of injecting the substances into living animals. At best, this is a very difficult method to use; at worst, it is useless. For the more certain, chemical type of measurement, we need large quantities of blood. It is almost impossible to carry out more than one or two of these measurements on any single animal because it would die from loss of blood. Of course, we want to be able to take a very small blood sample and quickly estimate the hormone concentrations in it. Until we can measure in this way hour-by-hour variations in concentration, most of our theories about control mechanisms can be little more than guesses.

If this is the case in the male, you can imagine what it must be like in the female, where the situation is even more complicated. It is made even worse by the fact that there are wide variations between species and what is true for one mammal may by no means be true for another. In very general terms, all female mammals have cycles of sexual behavior. At only one point in the cycle do they produce eggs from the ovary. At only one point in the cycle can sexual intercourse with a male produce an embryo. Again speaking in general, the cycle can be divided into two halves. In the first half, the egg is prepared in the ovary and the uterus is prepared to receive the egg. This half of the cycle culminates in the release of the egg from the ovary. Since it may take some time for the egg to be fertilized and to reach the uterus, the preparation of the latter may go on for a period after ovulation. The uterus increases in size and its surface layers become greatly thickened. If fertilization does not take place, in some animals the changes reverse and the uterus becomes smaller. In others, the top layers of the uterine wall break away and bleed in the process known as menstruation. Once this is all over, the cycle starts again. Another egg, or set of eggs, is prepared in the ovary and the uterus is again made ready to receive an embryo. The length of the cycle varies from a few days in a mouse to about a month in the human. Many, in fact, most, wild mammals have only one breeding season a year. Humans and many tame animals, on the other hand, can breed all the year round. There are such wide variations that it is very difficult to compare the processes in two different mammals. For obvious reasons it is impossible to do most experiments on human beings. We have to rely on rabbits, rats, or if we are lucky, on monkeys and chimpanzees for our experimental information. We can never be quite certain that what we see in these animals is also true of the human being.

However, the female cycle is such an important subject that it is worth making some attempt to describe what happens. Once again we are in trouble because we cannot take a small drop of blood and assess the amounts of progesterone, estradiol, LH, and FSH in it. Most of the data on the rates of hormone secretion comes from measurements of their excretion in the urine. At best, this is only a very indirect method. The diagrams of possible changes of hormone levels in the blood are very, very rough indeed. When accurate methods become available, they will probably have to be completely revised.

Early in the cycle, the FSH secretion is high and this encourages the growth and maturation of eggs in the ovary. LH then begins to rise. At this stage, little or no progesterone is being made by the ovary. The LH does not alter this, but it does in-

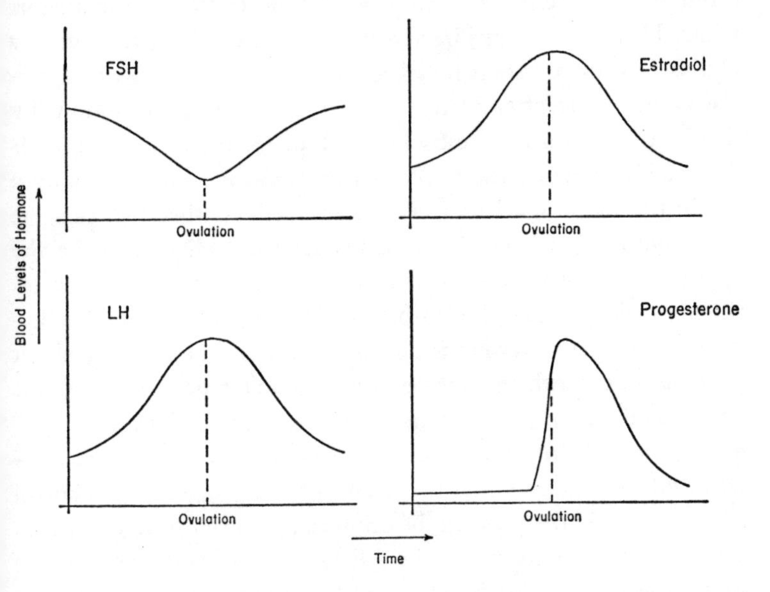

▸ FIGURE 18–1. Diagrams showing the approximate variations in blood levels of FSH, LH, progesterone, and estradiol during the female cycle. The scales are completely arbitrary.

crease the output of estradiol. There is no doubt that estradiol slows down the flow of FSH from the pituitary. The rising estradiol therefore lowers the blood level of FSH and stops the development of any more eggs in addition to the ones which are already on their way. Then just before the egg is ready to be released, progesterone begins to appear. It is probably secreted by cells in the ovary which lie around the egg. Most people believe that, at this stage, LH stimulates progesterone output. Why it should do so at this time but not at the beginning of the cycle is obscure. A higher level of LH may be needed to stimulate progesterone output than to stimulate estradiol output. The required LH blood level may not be reached until the time of ovulation. Alternatively, the progesterone-secreting cells may not be fully developed at the beginning of the cycle. We just do not know. When the egg leaves the ovary and goes down to the uterus, the manufacture of estradiol and progesterone continues for a short while. However, if fertilization does not take place, the outflow of these hormones soon falls back to a low level. This is a crucial point in any attempt to explain the cyclic mechanism. Why should the outflow of estradiol and progesterone slow down? Since LH stimulates the outflow, the reason is almost certainly a fall in the blood level of LH. But this only pushes the question one stage further back. What depresses the LH? It may be the appearance of progesterone. If this is true (and at present it seems the most likely idea), the lag between the rise of LH and the appearance of progesterone is all important. If LH brought about progesterone synthesis right at the beginning of the cycle, the LH would never get the chance to rise any higher. In consequence, no rise in estradiol level and no female cycle would occur. Only when we know the details of the progesterone control mechanism will the problem be unraveled. To return to our story, whatever may be its cause, the fall in estradiol and progesterone forms the last link in the chain. FSH output rises again and the cycle goes on.

The difficulties in explaining the cycle emphasize our estimation problems. Until we can measure accurately the hormone concentrations in the blood, we cannot prove either the outline just given or any other hypothesis. Nor can we say anything definite about the precise way in which the control operates. Again there are people who hold that the ovarian hormones feed back by acting on the pituitary gland cells themselves and others who believe that the interaction is an indirect one via the hypothalamus. Again it is possible that both schools are correct. While few workers would be prepared to state this categorically, it does seem that estradiol is primarily concerned with governing FSH output, while progesterone is primarily involved with LH. This is very important. Since LH stimulates the ovary to produce estradiol, high levels of estradiol could never result if estradiol suppressed LH release. As soon as the estradiol levels began to climb, LH outflow would fall and, in consequence, the estradiol would sink back again. We should get the same situation as in the testis, and there would not be any cyclic variation. If you look at Figure 18–1, you will see that the rise in LH seems to go on until just after ovulation. The beginning of its fall coincides approximately with the peak progesterone level. Can this be coincidence? It may be, but it does appear reasonable that the progesterone should suppress the LH output. If this is so, the crucial question is why progesterone should be at such a low level at the beginning of the cycle and then should suddenly rise about the time of ovulation. The levels of estradiol are at their peak at this time. Could this have anything to do with it? Recent biochemical work has shown that estradiol can alter the activity of several enzymes. If, at high levels, the estradiol modified the actions of certain ovarian enzymes, this might cause progesterone to be produced. This is pure speculation and we must admit that we just do not know. Many, many more experiments need to be done. But this is the stuff of science. Someone dreams up an idea which is then tested by practical work in the laboratory. Both the dreams and the practical experiments are necessary. Who knows? One day the dreams may come true.

You have probably been very confused by my attempted description of the female sex cycle. Science, however, is like this. A subject which is changing and progressing is confusing. It is only when an idea is definitely established that it becomes clear. In this case, it may help if I draw all the observations together here in an attempt to give a coherent account of the stages in the cycle.

(1) At the beginning of the cycle, estradiol and progesterone levels are low. FSH is high and LH, because of the absence of progesterone, is rising.

(2) The rising LH increases the output of estradiol which, in turn, depresses FSH levels. The low FSH does not allow any more eggs to develop.

(3) LH raises the estradiol levels to such an extent that the action of certain ovarian enzymes is modified and progesterone appears.

(4) The eggs are released.

(5) The progesterone begins to suppress the LH. The fall in LH lowers the output of both ovarian hormones.

(6) The low estradiol allows FSH to rise and the cycle begins again.

It is even possible that the feedback mechanisms are relatively unimportant and that the cyclic changes in FSH and LH are governed entirely by the hypothalamus without much reference to the blood levels of the ovarian hormones. However, most of the evidence indicates that the hypothalamus does take notice of progesterone and estradiol in the female and testosterone in the male. It is interesting that, in the male, FSH and LH do not appear normally to fluctuate independently of each other. The one hormone, testosterone, seems to control them both. In the female, estradiol suppresses FSH, while progesterone seems to control LH. The two pituitary hormones fluctuate independently. If this is so, it must mean that the hypothalamus can distinguish between the two very similar molecules of progesterone and estradiol. Estradiol acts on one mechanism; progesterone acts on the other. Testosterone, in contrast, may act on both mechanisms. Why should this be? We do not know, but it may be significant that testosterone appears to be half a progesterone molecule and half an estradiol molecule and has some of the properties of both. Can this account for the idea that testosterone controls both FSH and LH, while each ovarian hormone suppresses one pituitary hormone? Perhaps. The word sums up our state of knowledge. We must close this section by emphasizing yet again that much of it is pure speculation. It will be a long time before we can work it all out.

PREGNANCY

If anything, the hormonal control of pregnancy is even more complicated than that of the female sex cycle. You have been warned. If fertilization of the egg occurs, the production of estradiol and progesterone remains high. In the early stages, this is at least partially due to the action on the ovary of another an-

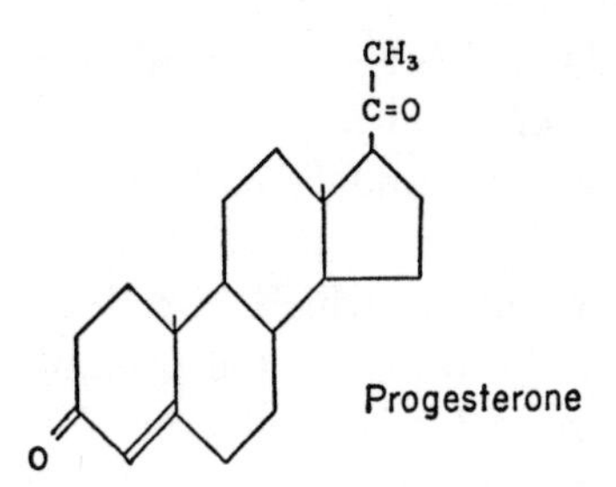

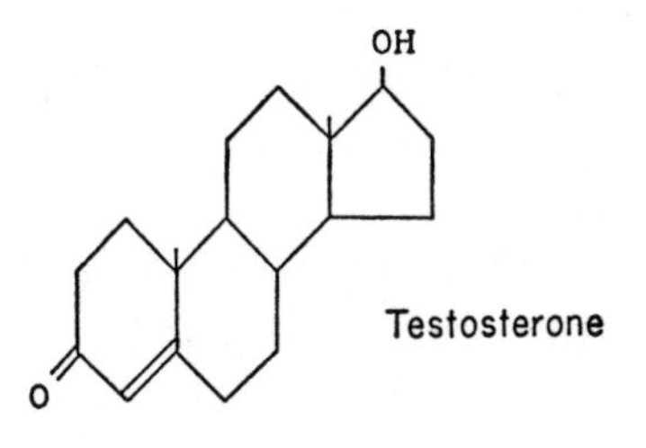

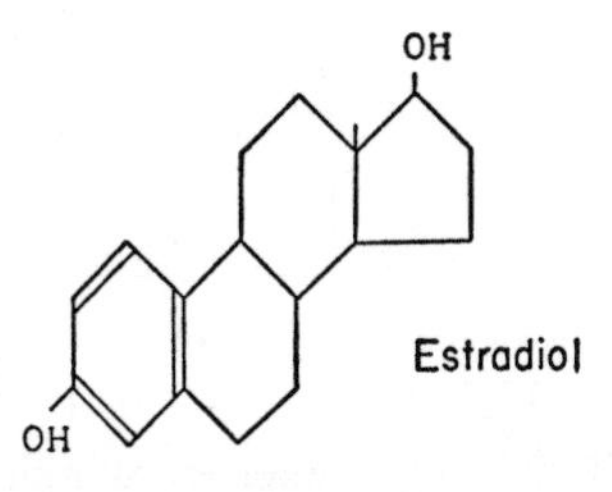

▶ FIGURE 18–2. The molecular structures of progesterone, testosterone, and estradiol. The left-hand ends of progesterone and testosterone are identical. The same is true of the right-hand ends of the molecules of testosterone and estradiol.

terior pituitary hormone, prolactin. The embryo then becomes embedded in the wall of the uterus and a structure known as the placenta develops. This acts as the intermediary between the mother and the developing child. It transfers food and oxygen to the child and carries away carbon dioxide and waste products. It also acts as an additional endocrine gland. Very soon it begins to secrete a hormone of its own which is similar to LH. It helps the ovary to continue to produce estradiol and progesterone. But the placenta is not content with this. It begins to make its own progesterone and estrogens, which, in action, are very similar to estradiol. As the embryo grows, the placenta gradually appears to take over the reproductive endocrine functions of both the ovary and the pituitary. In many animals, after about the half-way stage in pregnancy, it is possible to remove both the ovary and the pituitary without killing the young. This may give you some idea of how important the placenta becomes.

What is it that brings about birth? What makes the uterus, which has been quiet, suddenly to start contracting and expel the young animal from inside the mother? The uterus is made of unstriated muscle which has certain special properties. When it is stretched, it becomes more excitable and tends to contract. When it is bathed in estrogens, the actual contraction mechanism increases in bulk and becomes more powerful. When the muscle is acted upon by oxytocin, a posterior pituitary hormone, it tends to contract strongly. All these factors operate toward the end of pregnancy. The uterus is greatly stretched by the baby animal, the concentration of estrogens is high, and oxytocin is released from the pituitary. Despite all this, it is perhaps progesterone which holds the key. Progesterone stabilizes the membrane potential of a smooth muscle fiber and makes the fiber inexcitable. Toward the end of pregnancy, the high concentrations of progesterone seem to hold in check all the other factors which would make the smooth muscle contract. It is very likely that just before birth the progesterone levels in the uterus mysteriously fall. This allows all the other factors to come into play, the uterus contracts, and the baby is born. What causes this strange fall in progesterone level is totally unknown.

Before we leave this question of birth, we must discuss one more hormone. In most female mammals, the birth canal from the uterus to the outside world is very narrow and passes between the hard pelvic bones. If the uterus contracted strongly, and forced the baby into this canal, the baby would probably be killed. But fortunately, before birth, the canal becomes modified. Relaxin, a hormone made by the ovary and possibly also by the placenta, softens the bones of the pelvis and loosens the ligaments which bind those bones together. It also makes softer all the tissues lining the canal. The baby animal can pass out relatively easily and without damage. The more we learn about the intricate mechanisms which keep our bodies running, the more we should be surprised, not by the fact that they must stop in the end, but by the fact that they ever get going to start with.

LACTATION

Baby mammals are born in such a state that they are quite unable to fend for themselves. They rely entirely on their mothers for food and protection. During the first few months of their lives, the babies are usually fed by their mothers with milk from the mammary glands. In human beings, the breasts first begin to develop and grow at the time of puberty, when a girl grows up to become a woman. But until a woman becomes pregnant, her breasts remain inactive and do not produce any milk. During the later part of pregnancy, however, the milk secretion mechanism becomes fully developed. By the time the infant is born, the breasts are fully prepared to provide it with milk.

This preparation of the breasts near the end of pregnancy requires a remarkably large number of hormones. Most experiments have been done on lower mammals, but it is likely that, at least in broad outline, the results are applicable to human beings. Many of the experiments involve injecting hormones into nonpregnant animals in an effort to imitate the effects of pregnancy on the breasts. The first thing to note is that both estrogen and progesterone are essential for producing an increase in the quantity of breast tissue. Neither estrogen nor progesterone alone can bring about the desired result. In an otherwise normal animal, progesterone and estradiol injections can enlarge the mammary glands in a very similar way to that seen in pregnancy.

If these experiments are carried out in animals whose pituitaries have been removed, by now you will not be surprised to hear that the development does not take place. Nor is it brought about by additional injections of LH and FSH. Clearly some other hormonal influence must be necessary. It now seems certain that STH, TSH, and ACTH all play important parts. Without them the breasts could not develop. Whether they play a more specific role than they do in all growing tissues, or whether this is one example of a general property of these hormones is not known. What is known is that another anterior pituitary hormone called prolactin does act specifically on the breasts and is vitally important. It is essential for their full growth, and plays the leading part in maintaining the secretion of milk after birth. In most mammals, the placenta plays as important a role in the preparation of the breasts as it does in the development of the baby. It secretes a high proportion of the necessary progesterone and estrogen and also makes a hormone very similar to prolactin. It is remarkable that such a versatile endocrine gland should grow, develop, and die in a period which, in the human being, lasts a mere nine months or so.

After birth, the mechanisms for milk secretion which have been held in check, as it were, are suddenly released. A little milk may be made before the end of pregnancy, but it is not until the child has been delivered that the full flow begins. This is apparently because progesterone, and possibly estrogen, while they are vital for building up the secretory mechanism, do not allow it to work. Immediately after birth, the blood concentrations of these hormones fall rapidly and leave the breasts free to produce milk.

Confusion is often caused because people fail to realize that the secretion of milk into the ducts of the breasts, and the ejection of milk from those ducts, are quite separate processes. In this section, we shall discuss the first of these, milk secretion. Several workers have shown that the stimulus of suckling lowers the prolactin content of the pituitary. If the nipples are anesthetized, suckling has no effect. This apparently is another mechanism where the nervous and endocrine systems combine together to produce the desired result. Without the nervous stimulus of suckling, prolactin ceases to be poured out from the anterior pituitary. As a consequence, milk secretion ceases. So long as suckling goes on, prolactin maintains milk secretion. This can continue for fantastically long periods; in some Himalayan regions, children obtain milk from their mothers until they are five or six years old.

The connection between suckling and milk secretion has been shown by a very clever experiment. Suppose that, in a rat, we divided the nipples into two sets, A and B. We then cut the nerves supplying set A, while leaving set B intact. Suppose we allowed a litter to suckle at set A, the denervated nipples, only. The baby rats would be quite unable to get any milk. Both sets of glands would revert to their resting level and cease to make milk. The young would die. On the other hand, suppose we allowed the rats to suckle only at set B, the intact nipples. Lactation in all the glands would continue and, if we let them, the babies would be able to get milk from the denervated nipples as well as the intact ones. The litter would grow up quite normally. What does this experiment mean? In the first case, there is no nervous stimulus, and the pituitary cannot be stimulated to produce prolactin. In the second case, the suckling makes the pituitary secrete prolactin. Since the hormone is carried in the blood, it goes to all the mammary glands, not just to the ones with intact nipples. All the glands secrete milk. This is one of the clearest cases which illustrates the function of the pituitary stalk vessels. Prolactin is made by the anterior pituitary and this has no effective nervous connection with the brain. The only way in which nervous impulses can alter prolactin output is by controlling the release of some transmitter substance into the stalk blood vessels.

MILK EJECTION

The confusion between milk secretion and milk ejection is increased by the fact that one of the stimuli which brings about ejection is the same as the one which causes secretion—suckling of the nipples. This is well known to farmers, especially those who always milk their own cows by hand. A cow whose udder is obviously full of milk will not eject that milk until the teats have been manipulated for a few moments. There is a definite delay before the milk suddenly pours out. We have seen that prolactin stimulates milk secretion. While suckling encourages prolactin release, the hormone continues to bring about milk secretion even when suckling has temporarily stopped between feeds. Milk ejection is a much more short-term affair, and takes place only while suckling is actually going on. The nervous stimulus to ejection is clearly shown by the experiment of putting local anesthetic on the nipples of glands which are distended with milk. Even though the milk is there, a suckling litter is quite unable to obtain it.

Surrounding each breast duct, there are special cells which look rather like interwoven baskets. While they are not muscle cells, they can contract. When they do, they will clearly decrease the diameter of the ducts, and thus force milk out of the breast. Very ingenious experiments have been carried out in which the actual pressure inside the ducts was measured. In the resting gland, the pressure was quite low, but within 30 to 90 seconds of beginning suckling, the pressure suddenly rose and milk was ejected. Once again, by anesthetizing half an animal's nipples, it could be shown that while the stimulus was nervous, the response was hormonal. Suckling an intact nipple resulted in milk ejection from all the glands. This time a posterior pituitary hormone is involved. It is oxytocin, the same one that helps to make the uterus contract during birth. Direct observation has shown that putting oxytocin on the basketlike cells causes them to contract. There can be little doubt that oxytocin is essential for milk ejection.

Confirmatory evidence is provided by stimulation of the nerve tracts going to the posterior pituitary. Within about 20 seconds, this is followed by ejection of milk from the glands of a nursing mother animal. Injection of oxytocin into the blood produces the same response with approximately the same time lag. The nervous and endocrine systems combine together beautifully to bring about both milk secretion and milk ejection.

19 Beyond Voluntary Control

Have you ever had to give a speech in public or have you ever played in an important school or college game before a large crowd of people? If you have, or indeed if you have ever been afraid or excited in any way, you will know that under these circumstances things happen to your body over which you yourself have no control. Your heart begins to pound away like some old steam engine trying to drag a heavy line of trucks up to the top of a steep hill. Your hands become wet and clammy with sweat, and your face alternately flushes and goes pale. You so desperately want to appear in control of the situation and to show the people around you that you are quite calm. But somehow it doesn't work out that way. You are completely helpless. You cannot voluntarily do anything to control that pounding heart, those sweaty hands, and that flushed face. What causes these infuriating changes, and what use are they to your body? They are mainly the responsibility of the adrenal medulla and the autonomic nervous system.

Before we can properly understand how the medulla and the autonomic system work, we must first learn something about their anatomy. Physiologists often despise anatomists and anatomists often despise physiologists, but both subjects are vitally important for the understanding of the animal body. The autonomic system sends nerves to the heart, to the smooth muscle of the gut, bladder, and genital organs, to all the glands associated with digestion, to the muscles which control the flow through the small blood vessels, to the sweat glands, and to a host of other places. The one thing that most of these glands and muscles have in common is that we do not seem to be able to control them voluntarily. No matter how hard we try, we cannot, by thinking, control the rate of beating of our hearts nor can we make ourselves sweat. These things are not controlled by the conscious actions of our brains. It is a very different situation from that which we found in striated muscles in earlier chapters of this book. We can control those muscles quite easily and have no difficulty in directing the most delicate movements. Yet the man who can order his hands and arms to carry out all the fantastic movements required in the playing of a piano concerto can no more alter his own heart rate than the piano could play the concerto all by itself.

The motoneurons which send impulses to striated muscles, as we saw in Chapter 12, have their cell bodies in the spinal cord. Their axons travel directly, without any interruption, to the muscle. An impulse starting in the spinal cord does not have to cross a synapse on its way to the end plate of a muscle fiber. For the most part, impulses in motoneurons can be consciously controlled. However, the impulses which leave the front of the spinal cord in autonomic fibers cannot be controlled in this way. They differ also in the fact that they have to cross a synapse before they reach the gland or smooth muscle cell for which they are destined. Their path from the spinal cord to these muscle or gland cells contains two neurons, not one. Conventionally, the autonomic system is divided into two parts, the parasympathetic and the sympathetic. The parasympathetic fibers leave the central nervous system from its two ends, the brain and the very lowest part of the spinal cord. The sympathetic fibers leave the spinal cord from all the regions in between. In the sympathetic system, the first neuron (preganglionic) is usually short. It synapses with the second one (postganglionic) in aggregations of nervous tissue

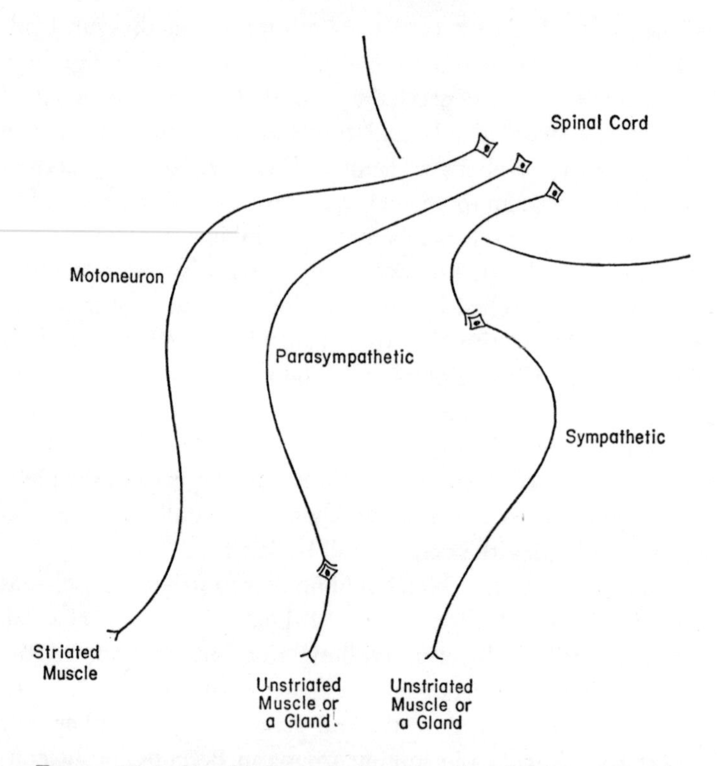

▶ FIGURE 19–1. Simple diagram showing the differences between a motoneuron and sympathetic and parasympathetic neurons in their pathways from the spinal cord. No attempt is made to show branching.

called ganglia which lie close to the spinal cord. On the other hand, in the parasympathetic the preganglionic neuron is usually long. It synapses with the second, postganglionic one close to the muscle or gland which the latter supplies. Each preganglionic neuron branches widely and supplies several postganglionic ones. There are therefore many more autonomic neurons leaving a ganglion than there are entering it.

What about the adrenal medulla which, likewise, is also beyond our voluntary control? In Chapter 17, we saw that each adrenal gland lies close to the kidneys and is made up of two parts, an outer cortex enclosing an inner medulla. The two parts are quite separate in function: the cortex is very sensitive to the action of ACTH while the medulla is not. Like the two lobes of the pituitary gland, the cortex and the medulla are completely different in the way in which they arise in the embryo. Indeed, in some primitive vertebrates, such as lampreys, and in some fish, the adrenal medulla and cortex remain separate throughout life. There is also another striking parallel with the pituitary. The cortex seems to be almost entirely without a nerve supply. Any nerve fibers which do reach it are probably more concerned with regulating the blood flow than with controlling the output of cortical hormones. In complete contrast, the medulla, like the posterior pituitary, has a very rich nerve supply. Every hormone-secreting cell seems to receive a nerve branch. The nerves, as you might have guessed, come from the sympathetic system. What you might not have guessed is that in the pathway from the spinal cord to the medulla there is only one neuron; there is no synapse between the central nervous system and the gland. The medullary cells are supplied only by sympathetic preganglionic neurons. They are the only cells in the body which have this sort of nerve supply. Is there any way in which we can explain this? There certainly is, and it is to be found in the way in which the cells of the adrenal medulla develop in the embryo. They arise from the same tissue that forms the postganglionic sympathetic neurons. In fact, we might almost describe the medullary cells as much modified postganglionic neurons. This is yet another example of the impossibility of making any sharp distinction between the nervous and endocrine systems. Before we go any further, we can make some generalizations about the chemicals which act as transmitters between pre- and postganglionic neurons and at postganglionic nerve endings. At all autonomic synapses the transmitter is acetylcholine, the same chemical which is released by motoneurons. All postganglionic neurons and, as you might expect, the cells of the adrenal medulla are activated by acetylcholine. Most parasympathetic postganglionic neurons also release acetylcholine. Most sympathetic ones release a chemical known as norepinephrine, perhaps mixed with a little of a closely related substance, epinephrine. The adrenal medulla secretes both norepinephrine and epinephrine. There is some evidence that different cells secrete the two hormones and that their proportion in the adrenal secretion is under nervous control. This is important because in some ways the two hormones have different effects.

Having disposed of rather a large number of slightly dreary facts, we can now turn to the more interesting problem of what the medulla and the autonomic system do. While it must not be taken too far, there is quite a lot to be said for the idea that the parasympathetic is concerned with the normal, everyday activities which are carried out when the animal is under no stress whatsoever from changing surroundings. The sympathetic and the adrenal medulla are more concerned with helping an animal respond to new situations. The impression is often given that this part of the system is active only in dire emergencies, but this is simply not true. The sympathetic is certainly vital in such situations, but much more frequently it is called into action in response to quite mild changes, such as a slight lowering of food intake or a slight alteration in the temperature of the surroundings. It is not active only when life and limb are in immediate danger. Many parts of the body, such as the heart, the eye, the salivary glands, the lungs, the gut, and the reproductive organs, receive both sympathetic and parasympathetic nerves. In most cases when this happens the two have opposite actions. The parasympathetic nerves, for example, encourage the secretion of digestive glands and the movements of the gut. The sympathetic stops gut movement. It causes certain circular muscles around the gut to contract tightly and to stop the contents passing along. The parasympathetic relaxes the muscle which guards the outflow of urine from the bladder. The sympathetic contracts the same muscle. The parasympathetic slows the heart, the sympathetic speeds it up. The parasympathetic constricts the iris of the eye. The sympathetic dilates the iris, allowing in as much light as possible. The cases could be multiplied. In every one, the parasympathetic encourages activities which can be carried out only when the animal is relaxed and at ease. The sympathetic discourages these activities. One does not want to have to go to the toilet when life is in immediate danger. Nor is it advisable in such circumstances for the heart to slow down and reduce the supply of blood to vital parts of the body.

Yet, sometimes the two systems combine to help each other. Both bring about secretion of the salivary glands. The parasympathetic probably increases the volume of the saliva, while the sympathetic increases the concentration of the active constituents in it. Both systems are also essential for sexual intercourse in the male. The parasympathetic brings about erection of the penis, while the sympathetic causes the sperm to be pumped out. But these are only limited examples. In many situations there is only just a sympathetic supply. The adrenal medulla, the sweat glands, the muscles which control the flow through most blood vessels, and the muscles which cause hairs to stand on end (goose flesh), are all supplied by the sympathetic system only. With the exception of the rather special case of the medulla, these muscles and glands are concerned with governing the rate of heat loss from the body.

Most of the autonomic postganglionic neurons differ from motoneurons in that the chemical transmitter which they release does not seem to be quickly destroyed. There is no highly efficient demolition mechanism like the cholinesterase at the junction between motoneurons and striated muscle fibers, As a result, a single nerve impulse may have quite a prolonged effect. A smooth muscle cell may contract, or a gland cell secrete, for a long time after nerve impulses have ceased to release the chemical transmitter. The transmitter cannot be removed or destroyed very rapidly at all. If this had not been the case, the whole idea of chemical transmission at nerve endings and between nerve cells might have taken much longer to come to light.

In 1920, Professor Otto Loewi was studying frogs' hearts. He could take the heart out of a frog's body and keep the heart beating by passing an oxygenated solution through it. He found that by stimulating the vagus nerve (part of the parasympathetic system) electrically, he could markedly slow down the beating of the isolated heart. But when he stopped the stimulation, the heart did not at once begin to beat faster. It took a little time to recover from the effect of the mass of impulses reaching it down the vagus nerve. Loewi wondered what on earth could be the cause of this. Why should the heart still beat slowly for a while, even after stimulation of the vagus had ceased? Could the vagus produce its effect by releasing a chemical which took some time either to be destroyed or to diffuse away? Loewi tested the possibility by a beautiful experiment which is a classic in the history of physiology. Instead of one heart, he used two which we shall call A and B. As usual, he passed an oxygenated solution through heart A. Instead of allowing this to run to waste as it came out of the heart, he collected it and passed it through heart B. He reasoned that, if the vagus worked by acting in some direct electrical way on the heart, heart B could not be affected by stimulating the vagus of heart A. On the other hand, if the vagus released a chemical which then slowed down the heart, with any luck this would pass into the solution passing through heart A. When it reached heart B, it might slow down its rate of beating also. Loewi stimulated the vagus of heart A. Heart B slowed down. From this very simple beginning arose all our modern studies on chemical transmitters.

THE ADRENAL MEDULLA

We have already mentioned that the chemical transmitter released by most sympathetic nerves is norepinephrine, although it is possible that very small quantities of epinephrine may also be involved. The adrenal medulla secretes both chemicals, the proportion between the two varying between the species and with the situation in which the animal finds itself. Because the cells are under direct nervous control, it seems possible to alter fairly quickly the proportions of the two hormones in the outflow from the gland.

It would clearly not be surprising if, in many ways, the effects of the medullary secretions were similar to those of the sympathetic system. Injection of norepinephrine into an animal's blood stream constricts the vessels in the skin, slightly speeds up the heart rate, and tends to inhibit the intestine. There are a number of other minor effects, but these are the most important ones. Norepinephrine has little effect on metabolism or on the blood flow through the liver and muscles. How does epinephrine, and therefore the adrenal medullary secretion, differ from this? Perhaps most strikingly, it differs in its action on the heart. Not only does it speed up the heart much more than norepinephrine does, it also makes each beat much stronger and more powerful. It is epinephrine that causes the pounding of your heart when you are frightened. While it may feel unpleasant, it is a most important adaptation to any stress. The blood is pumped round the body much faster. Organs such as the brain and muscles, which are vital when clear thought and rapid action are needed, are supplied with plenty of oxygen and energy-giving food materials. Your pounding heart is helping the other organs in your body to do a more effective job.

In a real emergency, when your muscles are tensed, the vital energy-giving glucose is rapidly used up and taken out of the blood. If you are not going to collapse quickly and if you are going to be able to make a prolonged effort, the blood glucose must be continually replenished. In the body much of the glucose is built up into the storage material, glycogen. The large molecules of glycogen are kept both in the liver and in the muscles. Before it can be used in the muscles themselves, or poured out from the liver to replenish the supplies in the blood, it must be broken down into much smaller and more manageable units. Epinephrine activates the mechanism which brings about this breakdown. It enables muscles to draw quickly on their own glycogen stores and enables the liver to keep up the levels of glucose in the blood. We have not yet finished with this remarkable compound, epinephrine. It helps the liver, muscles, and brain in another way as well. It makes the tiny blood vessels which run through these organs open up as widely as possible. This allows the actual flow of blood to be vastly increased. Glucose can be poured out from the liver and carried to the brain and muscles much more rapidly. Oxygen can quickly reach the active cells, while waste products can be hurried away. We must just outline one more action, although very little is known about it as yet. Epinephrine seems to activate that other great system which helps the response to stress, ACTH and the adrenal cortex. In some way it brings about the release of ACTH from the anterior pituitary and so completes the body's preparation for danger. Norepinephrine seems to be more concerned with milder mechanisms such as helping the body to deal with temperature changes and maintaining a normal blood pressure. In dangerous situations, the proportion of epinephrine in the adrenal secretion is probably increased. All this emphasis on trials and troubles must not lead us to forget that all the time the autonomic nervous system and the adrenal medulla are smoothly combining together. In a most efficient way, they run many aspects of our bodily functioning which are completely beyond our conscious control.

20 The Gut and Its Hormones

We really know very little about the detailed mechanisms which control the digestion of food and its passage along the gut. It is not an easy subject on which to do experiments. Many factors seem to be involved in the control of every single process. When a clear event does occur, it is often impossible to say which factor is responsible. The muscles and glands in the gut wall can even function to some extent in the apparent absence of nervous or hormonal control. While it is conceivable that this could be an illusion because we know so little of what is going on, it does seem to have some foundation. On the other hand, for smooth and efficient working, both the autonomic nervous system and a whole series of hormones seem to be essential. In the present chapter we shall be thinking mainly about the hormones which are involved.

The first gut hormone, secretin, was discovered as long ago as 1902 by E. H. Starling and W. M. Bayliss. It was to secretin that the word hormone was first applied. Bayliss and Starling were working on the pancreas, the big gland which pours digestive juices into the upper part of the small intestine. They anesthetized a dog, cut it open, and tied off a loop of the small intestine. The two physiologists then carefully cut all the nerves leading to this bit of gut, so that it was connected to the rest of the dog only by the blood vessels. The duct leading from the pancreas to the small

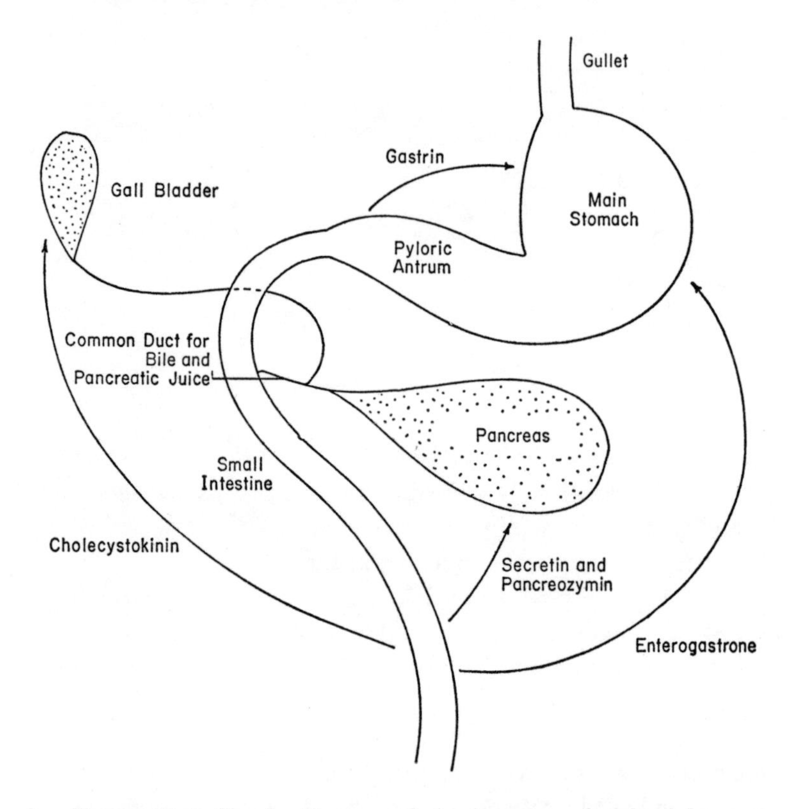

▶ Figure 20–1. Simple diagram of the hormones involved in controlling the activity of the gut.

intestine was exposed so that they could watch the flow of digestive juice coming from the gland. Bayliss and Starling then put some weak acid into the loop of intestine. They did this to imitate the stomach juices which are very acid when they first reach the intestine. To their surprise, the pancreas started to secrete its digestive juices freely. How could the stimulus of acid in the intestinal loop have brought this about? All the nerves which might have conducted impulses between the two tissues had been cut. The only way in which the stimulus of acid in the intestine could have caused the pancreas to secrete would have been by means of a hormone passing along the blood vessels. To test this, Starling cut off a piece of the intestine, ground it up, and filtered off the solid matter. He thus obtained a clear solution which he injected into the jugular vein of the dog. Once again the pancreatic secretions began to flow. The action of a hormone, carried by the blood, had been clearly demonstrated. It would be good if we could follow up this story with a detailed account of precisely how the hormone is released and how it acts on the pancreas. But we cannot. We have made some progress in the study of pancreatic secretion in the sixty years or so since the discovery of secretin, but there is still a very long way to go. We know now, for instance, that the acid secretions from the stomach stimulate the intestine to secrete two hormones which affect the pancreas, not one. Secretin, as we have seen, controls the volume of the pancreatic juice. The other hormone, pancreozymin, controls its enzyme content (enzymes are the protein substances which attack and digest the food). The vagus nerve can also control the enzyme content of the pancreatic secretions. In an intact animal, the nervous and endocrine systems work closely together to achieve the desired result.

In describing the discovery of secretin we have rather jumped ahead. The first process in digestion is, of course, the secretion of saliva, which is brought about by the autonomic nervous system. This is one of the cases where both parasympathetic and sympathetic work together. The parasympathetic controls the volume; the sympathetic, the enzyme content. Even the sight and smell of food can cause saliva to flow freely, as you yourselves must surely know. This seems to be a conditioned reflex. It is doubtful whether a baby would salivate on smelling a sizzling steak. It is a response that only takes place automatically when the smell has become clearly associated with a delicious meal to follow. The flow of saliva is increased when the food actually reaches the mouth. This, together with the sight and smell of the food, causes the vagus to fire off impulses which get secretion going in the stomach. When the food gets down there the stomach is, at least partially, prepared for it.

When the food is actually in the stomach, nervous reflexes increase the secretion of digestive juices. The stomach contracts rhythmically to grind up the food into a soft mass. It is here that we meet the first digestive hormone, gastrin. This is secreted into the blood by the region of the stomach nearest the small intestine, the pyloric antrum. The stimulus seems to be stretching and chemical stimulation due to the presence of the food. Carried by the blood, the gastrin passes to other parts of the stomach where it brings about an increased secretion of acid into the digestive juice. Odd though it may seem, this helps digestion, especially of proteins. Some of your occasional indigestion pains may be due to the acid contents of the stomach accidentally passing backward into the gullet. But, you may ask, how do we know that this is due to a hormone and not either to a nervous reflex or to a direct action of the food on the stomach itself? One basic technique is available whereby we can conclusively prove that a hormone is implicated. The variations on this theme are almost infinite, but the vital point is that they all eliminate the possibility of a nervous reflex being involved. The basis of all these experiments is the cutting away of a small portion of the stomach and the transplanting of this piece into some other region of the body. This completely destroys any nervous connection between the main part of the stomach and the transplant. Any influence which one has on the other must be carried by means of the blood. If we were to perform such an operation, and if we were clever enough surgeons, we could arrange matters so that we could collect the secretions from both the main stomach and the transplant. A favorite position for transplantation is the front of the abdominal wall. Suppose that we had been able to carry out these operations on a dog and had allowed the animal to recover completely. What would happen to the transplant if we allowed the dog to eat a meal? It would secrete a dilute acid solution. The only way in which this secretion could have been stimulated is by means of a hormone circulating in the blood stream. Thus we can prove the existence of gastrin.

This experiment clearly shows that food can release a hormone which causes an isolated bit of stomach to secrete. It tells us very little about the origin of the hormone. We might get some ideas by removing various pieces of gut and observing the effect on the flow of gastric juice. Nothing much happens until we remove the pyloric antrum. When this is removed, the flow of acid is very much less than usual. It seems possible that gastrin arises here, but how can we prove it? The answer is to make another isolated transplant, but this time of the pyloric antrum. Suppose we were to do this, and suppose we were also able to make arrangements for observing the secretions in the main part of the stomach. If we put food in the transplant or mechanically stretched it in some way, acid secretions would pour out into the main stomach. This shows that at least some of the gastrin must normally come from the pyloric antrum. In the intact stomach the secretion of acid seems to be a self-limiting process subject to feedback control. We can use our transplant to show this. If we put acid as well as food on to its surface, the main stomach fails to secrete. If we make the main stomach secrete by stretching the transplant, and then we add acid to the latter, the secretion stops. In a normal, intact animal, when food first enters the stomach, the food stimulates the pyloric antrum to secrete gastrin. This makes the stomach pour out acid which, in turn, slows down or stops the gastrin secretion. The mechanism ensures that excessive amounts of acid are not poured into the stomach. A breakdown in this control system may be one of the causes of the ulcers in the stomach and small intestine which are so common in the high-pressure conditions of modern life.

Several other hormones are concerned in the control of the gut. One, which goes by the exotic name of cholecystokinin, makes the gall bladder pour its bile into the small intestine. This helps the pancreatic juice to digest fats and counteract the acidity of the stomach secretions. Another hormone, enterogastrone (endocrinologists love long names), quiets down the stomach, decreasing the secretion of acid and slowing down the movements. Enterogastrone is released when the stomach contents first arrive in the small intestine. A failure of enterogastrone may be another factor in causing stomach ulcers, since such a failure would expose the stomach lining to excessive quantities of corrosive acid. Normally the lining is protected from ordinary concentrations of acid by a thick layer of mucus. However, large amounts of acid may break through this barrier, begin to eat away the stomach wall, and so cause an ulcer. Nervous factors are also undoubtedly involved in ulcer formation. The condition is most common in tense, overstrained, and hard-working people. If only we knew more details about the control of stomach secretions, we might be able to provide better answers to the problem of ulcers than we can at the moment.

THE PANCREAS

The secretions of the pancreas which reach the small intestine are clearly very important for digestion. Toward the end of the last century, it became apparent that the pancreas was important in a rather more sinister connection. Many people suffered from a disease known as diabetes mellitus. The Latin name indicated that sufferers secreted large quantities of urine which were sweet to the taste of anyone courageous enough to sample them. The disease had been known to the Romans. It invariably ended by the patient becoming thinner and thinner, going into a coma, and dying. Very little was known about the origin of the disease until 1889, when J. von Mering and O. Minkowski were working on the pancreas of a dog. To their surprise they found that removal of the gland produced symptoms very similar to those of diabetes mellitus. The condition was not due simply to poor digestion. It could not be brought on by tying off the pancreatic duct and preventing the secretions from reaching the intestine. When this was done, most of the pancreatic tissue degenerated, but little islands (known as the islands of Langerhans) remained healthy. Even in a healthy animal's pancreas, these islets could be easily distinguished from the rest of the gland. The obvious suggestion was made that they secreted a substance, the absence of which resulted in diabetes mellitus.

Many efforts were made to obtain this hypothetical substance which was given the name of insulin. Not until 1921 did two Canadians, F. G. Banting and C. H. Best, succeed in isolating an active extract. Most earlier workers tried to make an extract from the whole pancreas but the enzymes of the digestive juice destroyed the insulin. Banting and Best first of all tied off the pancreatic duct. They then left the animal until all the ordinary gland tissue had degenerated. Only then did they try to make an extract and they were successful. At last the answer to diabetes was at hand. Even today it is a common disease and is a nuisance, but it is no longer a killer. It can easily be controlled by injections of insulin, which is now universally available. Insulin itself is the most studied of all hormones. It is a protein and in 1954 became the first protein to have its chemical structure fully worked out. The broad outline of its actions has now been known for a long time but, as in so many cases, its detailed mechanism remains a mystery. However, that need not concern us here. The main symptom of insulin deficiency is a very high level of glucose in the blood. This spills over into the urine, thus making it sweet. Much more urine than normal is excreted in order to carry away the large amounts of glucose. The energy supply systems of the body cannot keep pace with this drain. The sufferer wastes away, passes into a coma, and dies.

The high blood levels in diabetes seem to be caused both by an overproduction of glucose and an inability to use that which is produced. Glycogen, the carbohydrate store, is broken down and the diabetic animal cannot build up the store again. Worse still, the body does not seem to be able to use glucose as a source of energy. In a last ditch effort to provide some energy, both proteins and fats are broken down. Both muscular and fatty tissues waste away. Eventually, the nervous system can no longer obtain enough energy to run, the animal goes into a coma, and soon dies. Very dramatically, all these symptoms can be completely reversed by the injection of the appropriate dose of insulin. The blood glucose falls, the carbohydrate stores are built up again, the glucose can be used to supply energy, and the fats and proteins can be resynthesized. However, care must be taken not to give too much insulin. The blood glucose then goes to the opposite extreme. It falls to exceedingly low levels, the nervous system once again cannot obtain energy supplies, and the animal becomes unconscious. Both too much and too little insulin have the same result: they make an animal go into a coma.

We know very little about the control of insulin secretion. ACTH, epinephrine, and perhaps STH, seem, in some ways, to counteract its effects. In contrast to the pancreatic hormone, ACTH and epinephrine in particular tend to raise the blood glucose level. If the adrenals and pituitary are removed from a diabetic animal, there may be an improvement in the diabetes before the animal dies for other reasons. In an intact animal, the islands of Langerhans are able to respond to blood glucose changes and to counteract them by appropriate alterations in the output of insulin. If high levels of glucose are maintained artificially, in a fruitless struggle to reduce them, the islets pour out more and more hormone and eventually die from the effort. There are many such hints and suggestive experiments, but we must admit that our knowledge of the natural control of insulin secretion is very nearly zero. To the pure scientist, this is distressing, but millions of sufferers from diabetes would probably cry, "What does it matter?" They have been freed from a killing disease. For them, at least, science's triumph in the story of insulin is very nearly complete.

Postscript

And so we have come to the end of our short study of the internal communication systems that keep the animal body working. Much has been omitted, much greatly simplified. The cerebral cortex, the highest region of the brain, has been almost ignored. There is nothing about such fascinating topics as memory and learning. But the omission is deliberate. We know very little about these subjects, beyond a few tantalizing hints and suggestions. In a book of this kind there are few worthwhile things to be said about them. What I hope is that the simplified and reasonably clear treatment of nerves and hormones will encourage you to go on to more advanced books and more detailed study.

If you have learned nothing else from reading these pages, you may perhaps have come to realize how little we really know. Scientists today, like churchmen in the Middle Ages, often seem to have the reputation of knowing all there is to know. Nor are they themselves averse to fostering this impression. But it is a totally false picture. The great Sir Isaac Newton once said, "I do not know what I may appear to the world, but to myself I seem to have been only a boy playing on the sea-shore, and diverting myself in now and then finding a smoother pebble or a prettier shell than ordinary, whilst the great ocean of truth lay all undiscovered before me." For a biologist the picture might be even more devastating, that of a wanderer in the Sahara Desert picking up the occasional grain of sand and investigating its mysteries. How often do we become absorbed in our grains and forget the vast desert around us. We are at the beginning in our study of life.

The nervous system is a fantastically complex mechanism with more components than even the largest man-made computer. Its nerve cells are interconnected in the most intricate and delicate ways. At the moment, we are just starting to unravel the story of how single cells work and of how they transmit information from one to another. Our poor efforts at understanding the interactions of neurons stem from two almost equally unsatisfactory methods. On the one hand, we can record the activity of one cell at a time and then attempt to synthesize the information that we gather from a large number of experiments. On the other, we can record the mass effect of a large number of neurons discharging and then try to work out how individual cells contribute. Still ahead lies the enormous problem of trying to record simultaneously the activity of several interconnecting cells.

It is perhaps difficult for you to comprehend the problem involved in studying even the spinal cord, the simplest part of the central nervous system. It might help if you imagine what would happen to a being from another planet who tried to investigate an electronic device as simple as a television set with methods comparable to those which we use in neurophysiology. We might begin an investigation on an unknown part of the brain by cutting out that part and looking for the consequence; our visitor might start by cutting a few of the wires and removing a valve or two. We might continue by stimulating the region electrically with shocks ten, a hundred, or even a thousand, times larger than the electrical changes which normally occur in a single nerve cell; he, on the other hand, would feed current from the main supply into various parts of the set. Finally, we might get round to simply recording the activity of a single axon or a single cell body; he might measure the current flow in a single wire or in a valve. In the end, we would each try to add together all our pieces of information and work out how the mechanisms might operate. Do you think our friend would be very successful in understanding the television set? I think he would have to be both very clever and very lucky to get more than a few mystifying hints and suggestions. Nor should we expect to gain anything like a complete understanding of the nervous system with our currently available methods. In fact, it is quite remarkable that we should know as much as we do.

The problems posed by the study of hormones are just as great. In order even to begin to understand how hormones work, we should be able to measure hour-by-hour variations in their blood concentrations. For most of these substances, this ideal is just a dream. Indeed, often we can make very crude estimates of hormone blood levels only by measuring the amount stored in the gland or the quantity excreted in the urine. It is rather like trying to estimate the number of cars of a particular make on the roads by counting those at the factory and those on the scrap heaps. Since we cannot measure the blood levels of most hormones, it is hardly surprising that their detailed mechanisms of action are lost in obscurity.

Perhaps this all sounds rather depressing. But it is exciting as well. There will never be any lack of new fields to conquer in endocrinology and neurophysiology. There is still much to be done in the study of nerve conduction and synaptic transmission. The integration of activity in the spinal cord has only just been touched on. The cerebral cortex with its fascinating functions of learning, memory, and conscious thought is an almost totally unknown land. Here at least the days of exploration are not past. But neither are the difficulties of exploration. For those who are prepared to face the frustrations of months and years of wrestling with experimental problems, there is always the chance of seeing at last the coast of a new continent. In an earlier age of geographical exploration, Sir Francis Bacon wrote some words which may provide a fitting end to this book: "They are ill discoverers that think there is no land when they can see nothing but sea."

Index